PURPLE LEVEL

SPELL IT OUT

READING AND SPELLING PRACTICE

Globe
Fearon

Upper Saddle River,
New Jersey

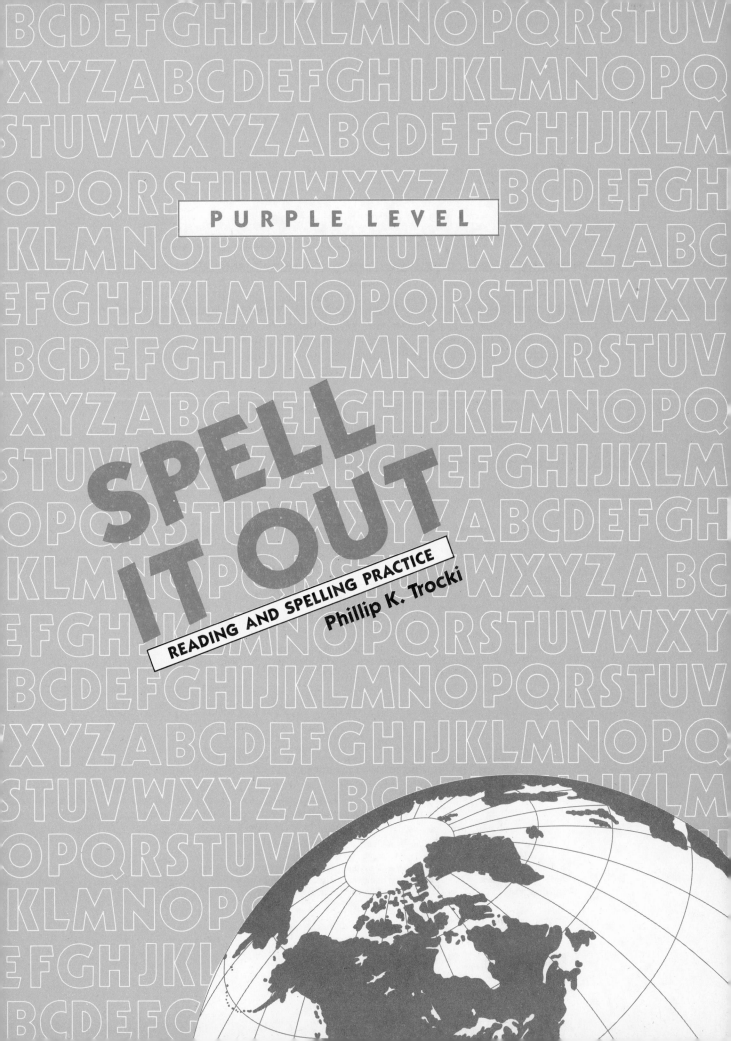

PURPLE LEVEL

SPELL IT OUT

READING AND SPELLING PRACTICE

Phillip K. Trocki

THE AUTHOR

Phillip K. Trocki, author of the four *Spell It Out* workbooks and co-author of the *A Need to Read* series, received his bachelor's degree in English and secondary education from Boston State College. He has taught English and reading for the Los Angeles Unified School District, and he has participated in the Writer's Program at the University of California at Los Angeles. For several years, Mr. Trocki was a staff member of the *New York Times*. He is currently assigned as a studio teacher in Los Angeles, and he has most recently written *Spelling Workout*, an eight-volume spelling series for Modern Curriculum Press.

PHOTO ACKNOWLEDGMENTS

Page 1, 4: © Outline Press/Brian Quigley; 2, 74: Ron Galella; 9: AP/Wide World Photos; 10: Fred Lewis/Virginia Watland; 12, 98: Fred Lewis/Krainin; 17: Outline Press; 18: Globe Photos/Ralph Dominguez; 20: Robert Mathieu/Retna Ltd.; 25, 26, 28: Int'l Paper co.; 3: Leo de Wys; 34: Leo de Wys/Francine Keery; 36, 76, 145, 146: AP/Wide World Photos; 41, 42, 44: American Egg Board; 49: William McIntyre/Photo Researchers; 50: Larry Mulvehill/Photo Researchers; 52: Harriet Gans/The Image Works; 57, 58, 60: © The Company of Art; 65, 66, 68: NOAA; 73: H. Armstrong Roberts; 81, 82, 84: American Cancer Society; 89: UPI/The Bettmann Archive; 90, 92: Christopher Lark/Lark Assoc., Inc.; 97: The NYT/Keith Meyers; 100: FPG Int'l/Trix Rosen; 105: The MOMA Film Stills Archive; 113: FPG Int'l/Peter Karas; 114: Rhoda Sidney; 116: NYU School of Dentistry; 121, 124: © Rick Reinhard; 122: Brian Lanker; 129, 130: Gamma Liaison; 132: Trans World Airlines, 137, 138, 140: Courtesy Dept. of Library Services/American Museum of Natural History; 148: Slick Lawson/Time Magazine; 153: Ellen Petty; 154: Tennessee Valley Authority; 156: Fred Lewis/Harold M. Lambert.

Spell It Out, Purple Level, Second Edition
Phillip K. Trocki

ISBN: 1–5567–5352–7

Printed in the United States of America
  12 13 14 15 04 03 02 01

TO THE STUDENT

Spell It Out, Purple Level is designed to give you practice in reading and spelling. Both are skills you need to communicate with other people.

Each unit is divided into two parts. First, in Developing Reading Skills, you will find a short story about an interesting topic or personality. Some subjects you may already know about. Others may be totally new to you. In any case, read the story, paying attention to the details and the point the author is trying to make. Then answer the questions that follow without looking back to the story for help.

The second half of the unit deals with Developing Spelling Skills. The words you will be working with are ones that you use every day. In fact, many of the examples have been taken from the story that you just read. A few rules of spelling will be explained in the lessons. There are, unfortunately, exceptions to the rules. Some words will have to be memorized. Try to memorize them before you begin the exercises. That way, you will have more practice writing the words correctly. If you do spell a word wrong, don't be discouraged. Some words are harder to spell than others. Just try to find out what it is about the word that makes it hard to spell. Keep that in mind when writing the word again.

Above all, enjoy yourself when using this book—that's what learning is all about!

CONTENTS

Roseanne

"Even when very young, I knew that I would be one person in a long line of storytellers," says Roseanne Barr. "I'd be one of those people with notebooks and old cardboard boxes full of handwritten tales." Audiences everywhere now recognize her as the wisecracking mom of the television show *Roseanne*.

As a real-life wife and mother, Roseanne has raised three children. Although she loves them very much, she can't seem to stop joking about them. "I do what it says on the aspirin bottle," she declares. "Take two—and keep away from children. I figure by the time my husband comes home, if the kids are still alive, I've done my job."

Even though her jokes make fun of housework and family problems, Roseanne has no complaints about her days as a housewife. "I liked it," she recalls, "There was a kind of really cool feeling about organizing things, cleaning, cooking, and caring for my family."

Even with all her household duties, Roseanne managed to keep up her writing. In her spare time, she wrote poetry and skits. There were so many that she had to store them in Hefty trash bags. Roseanne still writes today. With the publication of her autobiography, *My Life as a Woman*, Roseanne told her own life story. "I wrote the book to try to put my life in order."

If it was her family that Roseanne joked about, it was also her family that served as her first audience. One of her biggest fans was her younger sister, Geraldine, who persuaded Roseanne to try professional comedy. Geraldine helped Roseanne put her comedy act together by watching the audience's reactions. Geraldine took note of which jokes made people uncomfortable, and which made people laugh.

Roseanne's first job was in a Comedy Club in Denver. She performed after several other comedians who were insulting to women. Angered by their rudeness, Roseanne decided her act would be in defense of housewives like herself. The results are hilarious.

When asked to explain her sense of humor, Roseanne says, "I was just a real weird woman from the day I was born."

REVIEWING YOUR READING

Circle the letter beside the word or phrase that best completes the sentence.

1. Roseanne Barr says that she always thought that she would become a

   a. storyteller.
   b. housewife.
   c. mother.
   d. television star.

2. As a real-life mother, Roseanne has

   a. two children.
   b. six children.
   c. three children.
   d. four children.

3. In her spare time, Roseanne often

   a. wrote poems and skits.
   b. did housework.
   c. wrote jokes.
   d. performed for her children.

4. The person who persuaded Roseanne to try professional comedy was

   a. a writer.
   b. her mother.
   c. an agent.
   d. her sister.

5. Roseanne's first appearance as a comedian was

   a. on the *Tonight Show*.
   b. in a Denver Comedy Club.
   c. on television.
   d. in Las Vegas.

6. Roseanne's autobiography is titled

   a. *My Life as a Comedian*.
   b. *My Life as a Mom*.
   c. *Comedy Connection*.
   d. *My Life as a Woman*.

7. According to the story, you can come to the conclusion that Roseanne

   a. disliked taking care of her family.
   b. enjoyed caring for her family.
   c. had many family problems.
   d. often complained about housework.

8. You can come to the conclusion that Roseanne

   a. never did much writing.
   b. never did housework.
   c. wrote quite often.
   d. wrote mainly stories about children.

FIGURING THE FACTS

Decide whether the following statements are True or False. Write *T* on the line if the statement is true. Write *F* if the statement is false.

1. Roseanne always thought of herself as a writer. _____
2. Roseanne put the things she wrote into cardboard boxes. _____
3. Roseanne has written a novel about her sister. _____
4. Most of Roseanne's jokes were about acting. _____
5. Geraldine is Roseanne's cousin. _____
6. Geraldine helped Roseanne to form her comedy act. _____
7. Roseanne has written many poems. _____
8. Roseanne did not enjoy being a housewife. _____
9. Today, Roseanne has her own television show. _____
10. Roseanne has raised six children. _____

WHAT'S YOUR OPINION?

1. What do you think Roseanne means when she says, "I wrote my book to try to put my life in order"?

_____

_____

_____

_____

_____

2. Why do you think Roseanne was angered by the rudeness of comedians who insulted women?

_____

_____

_____

_____

_____

DEVELOPING SPELLING SKILLS

Study List	
Singular	**Plural**
autograph	autographs
cafeteria	cafeterias
celebrity	celebrities
ceremony	ceremonies
charity	charities
chocolate	chocolates
copy	copies
melody	melodies
opportunity	opportunities
personality	personalities
sandwich	sandwiches
stitch	stitches
territory	territories
vocalist	vocalists
wrench	wrenches

Let's review some of the ways singular nouns are made into plurals.

Rule: **Most words form their plural by adding *s* to the singular form.**

Example: Singular   Plural
            autograph   autographs

Rule: **But words that end in *ch* or *sh* form their plural by adding *es*.**

Example: Singular   Plural
            sandwich   sandwiches

Rule: **Words that end in *y* preceded by a consonant change the *y to i* before adding *es*.**

Examples: Singular   Plural
             charity   charities
             celebrity   celebrities
             melody   melodies

The Study List shows the singular and plural form of each word. It is most important to know both forms of these words.

SKILL DRILL 1

Change the following singular nouns to the plural form. Write your answers on the lines provided.

1. copy _____
2. melody _____
3. personality _____
4. stitch _____
5. autograph _____
6. wrench _____
7. chocolate _____

8. ceremony _____
9. opportunity _____
10. sandwich _____
11. territory _____
12. cafeteria _____
13. vocalist _____
14. charity _____

15. celebrity _____

SKILL DRILL 2

The following are short definitions of words from the Study List. Fill the blanks with words from the Study List that match the definitions. If you need help, check the Mini-Dictionary in the back of this book.

1. Help or relief for the poor _____
2. A formal or customary act like a wedding _____
3. A favorable chance _____
4. Singers _____
5. A loop of thread through cloth _____
6. Famous people _____
7. A duplicate or reproduction _____
8. Self-service restaurants _____
9. A person's signature _____
10. An area of land _____
11. Tools used to loosen or tighten bolts _____
12. The character of a person _____
13. Two pieces of bread with a filling _____
14. Tunes or songs _____
15. Candies made from cocoa _____

SKILL DRILL 3

Fill the blanks in each of the following words to form words from the Study List. Then write the word you have formed on the line provided.

1. person _ _ i _ _ es _____
2. sand _ _ ch _ _ _____
3. terr _ _ ories_____
4. _ _ enches _____
5. caf _ _ er _ _ s _____
6. char _ _ ies _____
7. cer _ _ on _ _ s _____

8. opp _ _ tun _ _ ies _____
9. sti _ _ hes _____
10. voc _ _ ists _____
11. autogra _ _ _ _____
12. c _ _ ebrit _ _ s _____
13. cho _ _ _ _ tes _____
14. mel _ _ ies _____

15. co _ _ _ s _____

SKILL DRILL 4

Fill in the charts below by writing the singular or plural form of the Study List words.

Singular	Plural
copy	
	ceremonies
wrench	
	cafeterias
melody	
	opportunities
stitch	
	charities

Singular	Plural
	autographs
personality	
	vocalists
chocolate	
	celebrities
sandwich	
	territories

WORD GAME 1

The words from the Study List are used in this puzzle. The numbers of the clues match the numbers in the puzzle. Read the clues below. Then write the plural form of the Study List word in the puzzle blocks.

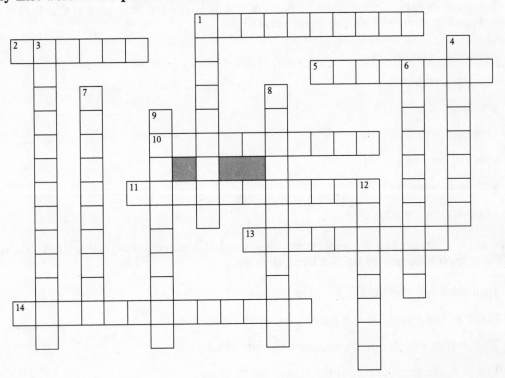

ACROSS

1. Customary acts
2. Duplicates or reproductions
5. Tools for tightening bolts
10. Signatures
11. Famous people
13. Singers
14. Characters

DOWN

1. Organizations that help the poor
3. Lucky chances
4. Tunes
6. Candies
7. Lunchtime food
8. Areas of land
9. Self-service restaurants
12. Loops of thread

Study List

Singular	Plural
autograph	autographs
cafeteria	cafeterias
celebrity	celebrities
ceremony	ceremonies
charity	charities
chocolate	chocolates
copy	copies
melody	melodies
opportunity	opportunities
personality	personalities
sandwich	sandwiches
stitch	stitches
territory	territories
vocalist	vocalists
wrench	wrenches

HOW WELL CAN YOU SPELL?

Try to take this practice test without looking back at Lesson 1. After you have finished, check your work against the Study List. Correct any mistakes you have made.

A. One word in each of the following pairs of words is spelled incorrectly. Circle that word and spell it correctly on the line provided.

1. cafaterias, celebrities   _____

2. charity, cerimony   _____

3. choclates, copies   _____

4. melodies, personalitys   _____

5. stitchis, territory   _____

6. vocalists, wrenchs   _____

7. sandwitches, opportunity   _____

B. In each of the following sentences, one word is spelled incorrectly. Find that word. Then spell it correctly on the line provided.

8. Josh asked all the singers for their autografs.   _____

9. Many of the people at the party were celebritys.   _____

10. The money was donated to Anne's favorite charitys.   _____

11. Please make three copys of the music for the band.   _____

12. There were many opportunitys to meet people at the dinner.   _____

13. All of the territorys south of this border are Mexican.   _____

14. As the audience entered, the vocalysts began to sing.   _____

15. Gregory has written many beautiful melodys.   _____

CHALLENGE WORDS

Use what you have learned in this lesson to help you remember how to spell the Challenge Words below.

wristwatches	universities	centuries
anxieties	agencies	assemblies
testimonies	theories	priority

Home on the Range

They can weigh up to 2,000 pounds and run at speeds of 40 miles per hour. They are armed with horns that grow to be two feet in length. We call them buffaloes, but their correct name is *bison*. In places like Yellowstone National Park, tourists are forbidden to go near the herds because so many people have been injured by them. Some people have even lost their lives. It seems that people and the bison have been at odds for quite some time.

There were once over 60 million bison in North America. Large herds roamed the plains from western Canada to as far south as Texas. As settlers moved west, they used bison meat in order to survive. Later, as farms sprang up, much of the land was cultivated. Most ranchers also raised cattle and other livestock. Between farmland and grazing land, however, there was no room for the huge wandering herds of bison. People were competing with bison for the open range. The solution was to eliminate the bison. Ranchers were forced to hire professional hunters, who killed the animals and took the hides.

Perhaps the most famous hunter during this period was William Cody. He was well known for his appearances in "Wild West" shows and rodeos. Cody hunted buffaloes to provide meat for the crews of workers who were building the railroads. That was how he earned his nickname—Buffalo Bill. Who knows, if people had referred to bison by the proper name, Buffalo Bill might well have been called Bison Bill!

Great numbers of animals were also killed just for the "sport" of it. Sport hunters took the horns as mementos. By 1890, there were only about 800 bison left in the wild. This crisis prompted the creation of the American Bison Society. Its members believed that they could save the species that was threatened with extinction. They worked diligently to set aside lands for the bison herds. Eventually, the bison population began to increase. The society opened many other protected lands throughout North America. Today there are about 30,000 bison in the wild. But this figure is very small compared with the 60 million that once roamed our lands.

REVIEWING YOUR READING

Circle the letter beside the word or phrase that best completes the sentence.

1. Bison can often

   a. weigh up to 2,000 pounds.
   b. have 10-foot horns.
   c. weigh up to 4,000 pounds.
   d. have 8-foot horns.

2. In places like Yellowstone National Park, people are

   a. allowed to pet the bison.
   b. encouraged to feed the bison.
   c. forbidden to go near the bison.
   d. allowed to ride the bison.

3. The settlers who moved west used the bison for

   a. transportation.
   b. pets.
   c. food.
   d. pulling heavy loads.

4. A large part of the settlers' land was used for

   a. bison grazing.
   b. crops and cattle.
   c. railroads and crops.
   d. cattle and roads.

5. According to the selection, you can conclude that

   a. there was plenty of land for people and bison.
   b. there was not enough land for people and bison.
   c. people just did not like the bison.
   d. bison killed many settlers in the 1890s.

6. The solution was to eliminate the bison. The word *eliminate* means

   a. feed.
   b. save.
   c. transfer.
   d. kill.

7. To solve the bison problem, the settlers had to

   a. move to other lands.
   b. hire professional hunters.
   c. ship the bison to Europe.
   d. put the bison in pens.

8. You can conclude that the American Bison Society

   a. killed many animals.
   b. saved many of the bison.
   c. fought many of the settlers.
   d. used bison for food.

FIGURING THE FACTS

Decide whether the following statements are true or false. Write _T_ on the line if the statement is true. If the statement is false, change the statement to make it true. Cross out the incorrect word or phrase in the sentence. Then, if necessary, write the correct word or phrase on the line.

1. The _bison_ is the correct name for the American buffalo. _____

2. At one time there were over 60 billion bison in North America. _____

3. Bison roamed the plains of western Canada. _____

4. Settlers used horse meat to survive their first years. _____

5. Between farms and grazing land, there was no room for bison. _____

6. Professional hunters took the hides of the animals. _____

7. Great numbers of hunters were killed for the "sport" of it. _____

8. By 1890, there were only about 800 bison left in the wild. _____

9. The American Bison Society set aside zoos for bison to roam in. _____

10. Buffalo Bill was a famous bison hunter. _____

WHAT'S YOUR OPINION?

1. Do you think the slaughter of the bison could have been prevented? Explain.

_____

_____

_____

_____

2. Why do you think it is important to save different species of wildlife that are threatened with extinction?

_____

_____

_____

_____

DEVELOPING SPELLING SKILLS

Study List

Singular	Plural
belief	beliefs
buffalo	buffaloes
Eskimo	Eskimos
handkerchief	handkerchiefs
kangaroo	kangaroos
memento	mementos
mosquito	mosquitoes
portfolio	portfolios
spaghetti	spaghetti
species	species
thief	thieves
tomato	tomatoes
tornado	tornadoes
volcano	volcanoes
yourself	yourselves

Some words form their plurals irregularly. There are some guidelines for these words, but for the most part, they should be memorized.

Rule: When a noun ends in *o* preceded by a vowel, we always add *s* to form the plural.

Example: | Singular | Plural |
| rodeo | rodeos |

Rule: When a noun ends in *o* preceded by a consonant, we usually add *es* to form the plural.

Example: | Singular | Plural |
| buffalo | buffaloes |

However, there are exceptions to this rule.

Example: | Singular | Plural |
| memento | mementos |

Rule: When a singular noun ends in *f*, we sometimes add *s* to form the plural. Sometimes we drop the *f* and add *ves*.

Example: | Singular | Plural |
| belief | beliefs |
| life | lives |

Since there is no set rule for words ending in *f*, the plurals must be memorized.

Some words are the same in the singular as in the plural.

Example: | Singular | Plural |
| species | species |

If you memorize the singular and plural nouns in the Study List, you will be able to spell other words that form their plurals in a similar way.

SKILL DRILL 1

Change the following singular nouns to the plural form. Write your answers on the lines provided.

1. spaghetti _____
2. portfolio _____
3. buffalo _____
4. belief _____
5. volcano _____
6. tomato _____
7. memento _____

8. species _____
9. mosquito _____
10. Eskimo _____
11. yourself _____
12. thief _____
13. tornado _____
14. kangaroo _____

15. handkerchief _____

SKILL DRILL 2

The following are short definitions of words from the Study List. Fill the blanks with words from the Study List that match the definitions. Some of the definitions will require the singular form of the word, some the plural. If you need help, check the Mini-Dictionary in the back of this book.

1. A mountain that has erupted _____
2. An animal that hops and is found in Australia _____
3. The people who live near the North Pole _____
4. A large animal that roamed the plains of North America _____
5. A piece of cloth used for wiping your face _____
6. Large storms that have funnel-like clouds _____
7. A juicy, red fruit, often used as a vegetable _____
8. Someone who steals _____
9. A certain variety of something _____
10. A long, thin noodle _____
11. Cases for carrying important papers _____
12. Souvenirs _____
13. Flying insects that bite _____
14. You; your being _____
15. A strong feeling about something _____

SKILL DRILL 3

Fill the blanks in each of the following words to form words from the Study List. Then write the word you have formed on the line provided.

1. yoursel _ _ s _____

2. tornad _ _ s _____

3. thie _ _ s   _____

4. spag _ _ _ _ i _____

5. mosqui _ _ _ s _____

6. kangar _ _ s _____

7. bel _ _ fs   _____

8. volcan _ _ s _____

9. tomat _ _ s _____

10. spec _ _ s _____

11. portfol _ _ s _____

12. memen _ _ s_____

13. handkerch _ _ _ s _____

14. Eski _ _ s _____

15. buffa _ _ _ s_____

SKILL DRILL 4

Answer the following questions by using words from the Study List.

Which of the plural words end with *oes*?

1. _____   2. _____

3. _____   4. _____

5. _____

Which of the plural words end with *ves*?

6. _____   7. _____

Which of the words are the same in the singular as the plural?

8. _____   9. _____

Which of the singular words end with two vowels?

10. _____   11. _____

Which of the plural words end with *fs*?

12. _____   13. _____

Which of the plural words ends with *mos*?

14. _____

Which of the plural words ends with *tos*?

15. _____

WORD GAME 2

On the left are hints for the puzzle spaces on the right. If you provide the plural form of the correct Study List word, you will find the answer to the puzzle question by reading the shaded column downward. Write your answer on the line below.

BISON

BANDANNAS
YOU
INSECTS
CERTAIN VARIETIES

ERUPTING MOUNTAINS
SOUVENIRS

NOODLES
THEY STEAL
FEELINGS

CARRYING CASES
RED FRUITS
STORMS
HOPPING ANIMALS
THEY LIVE NEAR
   THE NORTH POLE

What has the bison finally found? _____

Study List

Plural
beliefs
buffaloes
Eskimos
handkerchiefs
kangaroos
mementos
mosquitoes
portfolios
spaghetti
species
thieves
tomatoes
tornadoes
volcanoes
yourselves

HOW WELL CAN YOU SPELL?

Try to take this practice test without looking back at Lesson 2. After you have finished, check your work against the Study List. Correct any mistakes you have made.

A. One word in each of the following pairs of words is spelled incorrectly. Circle that word and spell it correctly on the line provided.

1. Eskimoes, buffaloes _____

2. handkerchiefs, believs _____

3. kangaroos, mementoes _____

4. moskeetoes, portfolios _____

5. spaghetti, speshies _____

6. thiefs, tomatoes _____

7. volcanos, tornadoes _____

8. yourselfs, mosquitoes _____

B. In each of the following sentences, one word is spelled incorrectly. Find that word. Then spell it correctly on the line provided.

9. There was a time when millions of bufalos roamed the plains. _____

10. Tina gave her mother several linen handkerchieves. _____

11. In Australia, kangaroes roam freely. _____

12. The artists brought their portfolioes with them today. _____

13. For dinner we will have spagetti with meatballs and salad. _____

14. We grew tomatos and green beans in our garden this year. _____

15. Many tornados strike the state of Kansas each spring. _____

CHALLENGE WORDS

Use what you have learned in this lesson to help you remember how to spell the Challenge Words below.

tuxedos	sopranos	sheriffs
embargoes	echoes	avocados
broccoli	salmon	heroes

La Cantadora

La cantadora is Spanish for "the singer." It is a title that fits Linda Ronstadt perfectly. But Spanish? Most people know her as a rock star. Linda's album, *Canciones di mi Padre*, has established her as the reigning queen of Mexican music.

The album title means "Songs of my Father." The recording contains only mariachi music, the traditional music of Mexico. The word *mariachi* came from bands which played at weddings (marriage—mariachi). The songs are a type of Mexican country/western.

When Linda decided to record the album, she contacted Ruben Fuentes. He is the foremost arranger of mariachi music. When Linda handed him a list of the songs she wanted to sing, he asked, "Where did you hear of these songs?" "From my father," Linda replied. Ruben was doubtful that a rock singer could handle the exact sounds that were necessary. "But these songs are very difficult to sing," he said. "I know," answered Linda, "I'll practice very hard." And she did.

The experience of making the album offered Linda an ever greater challenge. That's because the verses are in Spanish. It's a language that Linda readily admits that she doesn't speak very well. For weeks, she worked to refine each song, one line at a time. Sometimes it would take more than three weeks just to perfect one song.

Linda has been called the most adventurous singer in American music. Her musical success has touched the world of rock, country, and even opera. Still, her records keep going platinum. She has received awards for her other albums, but these songs are special. "These are a complete release of another part of my heart." When asked exactly what part, she replies, "It's just my dad."

REVIEWING YOUR READING

Circle the letter beside the word or phrase that best completes the sentence.

1. Most people know Linda Ronstadt as

   a. a songwriter.
   b. an opera star.
   c. a rock star.
   d. a guitarist.

2. Mariachi is

   a. a Mexican songwriter.
   b. the traditional music of Mexico.
   c. Spanish for singer.
   d. the traditional music of Spain.

3. The person Linda contacted to help on her album was

   a. her grandfather.
   b. her father.
   c. Ruben Fuentes.
   d. her aunt Louisa.

4. Making the *Canciones* Album was especially difficult for Linda because she

   a. didn't know any of the music.
   b. couldn't remember the words.
   c. didn't sing with her favorite musicians.
   d. doesn't speak Spanish very well.

5. Ruben Fuentes is the foremost arranger of mariachi music. The word *foremost* probably means

   a. leading.
   b. most wealthy.
   c. intelligent.
   d. most formal.

6. Linda grew up

   a. in Mexico.
   b. near Tucson, Arizona.
   c. south of the Mexican border.
   d. in New Mexico.

7. You can conclude that Linda's family

   a. liked music.
   b. disliked music.
   c. were all professional musicians.
   d. sang on television.

8. You can conclude that Linda has been called an "adventurous" singer because

   a. she sings all kinds of music.
   b. she likes to do wild things.
   c. she has taken many trips to Mexico.
   d. her records keep going platinum.

FIGURING THE FACTS

Decide whether the following statements are true or false. Write *T* on the line if the statement is true. If the statement is false, change the statement to make it true. Cross out the incorrect word or phrase in the sentence. Then, if necessary, write the correct word or phrase on the line.

1. "La cantadora" means "the songs" in Spanish.   _____

2. Mariachi is like Mexican church music.   _____

3. Linda's father sings on her album.   _____

4. No one knows where the name mariachi came from.   _____

5. Linda speaks Spanish fluently.   _____

6. Sometimes it took Linda weeks to perfect one song.   _____

7. Ruben Fuentes helped Linda with the album.   _____

8. Linda's albums have received awards.   _____

9. Linda has sung rock, country, and even opera.   _____

10. The album title means "Songs of my Father."   _____

WHAT'S YOUR OPINION?

1. What do you think Linda means when she says, "These are a complete release of another part of my heart"?

    _____

    _____

    _____

    _____

    _____

2. Linda worked very hard to perfect the songs on her album, even though most people wouldn't recognize the mistakes. Why do you think she worked so hard?

    _____

    _____

    _____

    _____

    _____

DEVELOPING SPELLING SKILLS

Study List

achievement
ancient
beige
conceited
conscience
counterfeit
deceive
efficient
experience
forfeit
hygiene
neighborhood
received
reigning
sufficient

The following words appear in the reading selection.

received   experience   reigning

Notice that these words all have the vowel combination *ei* or *ie*. There is a simple rule for spelling these types of words, which you probably already know.

Rule: ***i* before *e*, except after *c*, or when sounded like *a* (ay) as in *neighbor* and *weigh*.**

> *i* before *e* as in *achieved,*
> except after *c* as in *received,*
> or when sounded like *a* (ay) as in *reigning.*

Like most rules, there are always exceptions that must be memorized. The word *height* is one of them, because the *e* comes before the *i*. Here are a few other exceptions that must be memorized:

> ancient   efficient   forfeit
> conscience   counterfeit

Try to remember the "*i* before *e*" rule when you are learning how to spell the words from the Study List.

SKILL DRILL 1

Write the following Study List words on the lines provided. Then circle the *ei* or *ie* in each word.

1. sufficient _____
2. efficient _____
3. conscience _____
4. ancient _____
5. beige _____
6. reigning _____
7. neighborhood_____

8. received _____
9. deceive _____
10. conceited _____
11. achievement _____
12. experience _____
13. hygiene _____
14. forfeit _____

15. counterfeit _____

SKILL DRILL 2

The following are short definitions of words from the Study List. Fill the blanks with words from the Study List that match the definitions. If you need help, check the Mini-Dictionary in the back of this book.

1. A place where people live _____

2. A light tan color _____

3. Very old _____

4. As much as is needed; enough _____

5. To have taken something into your possession _____

6. Ruling over people _____

7. Not genuine; fake _____

8. To give up as a penalty _____

9. To make someone believe that something false is true _____

10. Able to do something without waste _____

11. The sense of right and wrong _____

12. Knowledge that comes from doing something _____

13. Rules of good health _____

14. Having too high an opinion of oneself _____

15. An accomplishment or feat _____

SKILL DRILL 3

Fill the blanks in each of the following words to form words from the Study List. Then write the words you have formed on the line provided.

1. hyg _ _ ne _____

2. anc _ _ nt _____

3. ach _ _ vement _____

4. consc _ _ nce _____

5. rec _ _ ved _____

6. conc _ _ ted _____

7. effic _ _ nt _____

8. forf _ _ t _____

9. b _ _ ge _____

10. counterf _ _ t _____

11. suffic _ _ nt _____

12. r _ _ gning _____

13. dec _ _ ve _____

14. exper _ _ nce _____

15. n _ _ ghborhood _____

SKILL DRILL 4

Answer the following questions by using words from the Study List.

Which words are spelled with *ei* after the letter *c*?

1. _____   2. _____

3. _____

Which words are spelled with *ie* after the letter *c*?

4. _____   5. _____

6. _____   7. _____

Which words have the *a* sound (ay) as in *weigh*?

8. _____   9. _____

10. _____

Which words have *ie* after any letter but *c*?

11. _____   12. _____

13. _____

Which words have *ei* after any letter but *c*? (Write words you have not used yet.)

14. _____   15. _____

WORD GAME 3

This is a puzzle without clues! Study the length and spelling of each Study List word. Then figure out which words from the Study List fit in the spaces. Once you have found the first word, the rest will be easy to find. Some of the letters are given to you.

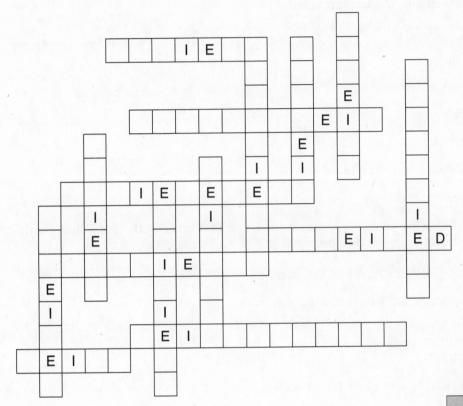

Study List

achievement
ancient
beige
conceited
conscience
counterfeit
deceive
efficient
experience
forfeit
hygiene
neighborhood
received
reigning
sufficient

HOW WELL CAN YOU SPELL?

Try to take this practice test without looking back at **Lesson 3**. After you have finished, check your work against the Study List. Correct any mistakes you have made.

A. One word in each of the following pairs of words is spelled incorrectly. Circle that word and spell it correctly on the line provided.

1. nieghborhood, ancient   _____

2. beige, acheivement   _____

3. concieted, forfeit   _____

4. sufficient, decieve   _____

5. efficeint, experience   _____

6. reigning, recieved   _____

7. consceince, hygiene   _____

B. In each of the following sentences, one word is spelled incorrectly. Find that word. Then spell it correctly on the line provided.

8. Diana will be the riegning queen of the pageant.   _____

9. The expereince we gained while working was quite valuable.   _____

10. The anceint writings revealed many secrets of the past.   _____

11. We discovered that the money he found was counterfiet.   _____

12. Good hygeine is essential to a happy life.   _____

13. Jason will have to forfiet the prizes he won.   _____

14. Alice's shoes were in shades of biege and black.   _____

15. One loaf of bread should be sufficeint for all of us.   _____

CHALLENGE WORDS

Use what you have learned in this lesson to help you remember how to spell the Challenge Words below.

grievance	masterpiece	perceive
unveil	yield	shrieking
surveillance	leisurely	disbelief

Bill Cosby's Helpful Hints

Everyone knows Bill Cosby. He's a TV star, a writer, and a parent. He also has a doctor's degree in education. This means that he knows quite a bit about teaching and learning. And he has some important things to say about reading. He wrote an article giving valuable hints for people who want to learn to read faster. Here are some of his suggestions.

"Read with a good light—and with as few friends as possible. . . . No TV, no music." Getting rid of distractions "will help you concentrate better—and read faster," says Bill.

For "heavy reading," such as nonfiction books, Bill recommends *previewing*. "Read the entire first two paragraphs of whatever you've chosen," he says. "Next read only the first sentence of each successive paragraph. Then read the entire last two paragraphs." You won't get all the details, but you will get an overall idea of what the piece is about.

For "light reading," such as popular magazines, Bill recommends *skimming*. To skim, move your eyes quickly across each line of type. "Pick up only a few key words in each line," suggests Bill. Try skimming the example below. The important words are circled.

> The (trouble) with (skimming) is that
> sometimes you only (get half) the (idea).

With a little practice, "you should be able to skim a weekly popular magazine . . . in less than half the time it takes you to read it now," Bill says. But like previewing, skimming only gives you a general idea.

Bill's last recommendation is the most useful for schoolwork. It helps you read faster and understand more. The technique is called *clustering*. You train your eyes to read in clusters, or groups, of up to three or four words at a time. Let's cluster a statement Bill Cosby makes in his article:

> "For most of us,   clustering is   a totally different way
> of seeing   what we read."

Reading in clusters takes constant practice. Here's what Bill suggests: "Pick something light to read. Read it as fast as you can. Concentrate on seeing three or four words at once rather than one word at a time. Then reread the piece at your normal speed to see what you missed the first time." Learning to cluster takes time. It's worth it if you think of how much time you'll be saving on things you have to read. Thanks, Bill!

REVIEWING YOUR READING

Circle the letter beside the word or phrase that best completes the sentence.

1. Bill Cosby has a doctor's degree in

   a. television.
   b. education.
   c. medicine.
   d. reading.

2. To help you concentrate on your reading, you should

   a. circle all important words.
   b. get rid of distractions.
   c. work with a few friends.
   d. have music playing.

3. To get an overall idea of what a book is about, you should

   a. read the first chapter.
   b. preview.
   c. skim the first chapter and the last page.
   d. read the last chapter.

4. Previewing is useful for "heavy reading," such as

   a. short stories.
   b. nonfiction books.
   c. popular magazines.
   d. clusters.

5. Moving your eyes quickly across each line of type is called

   a. clustering.
   b. previewing.
   c. skimming.
   d. light reading.

6. Both skimming and previewing give you

   a. a general idea of the material.
   b. all the details.
   c. practice in clustering.
   d. practice in reading one word at a time.

7. Clustering is the technique that is most useful for schoolwork. The word *technique* means

   a. practicing.
   b. skimming.
   c. a certain way of doing something.
   d. a good way to read.

8. According to the article, you can conclude that clustering helps you

   a. read slowly and remember more.
   b. read faster and remember more.
   c. memorize groups of words.
   d. get half an idea of the material.

FIGURING THE FACTS

Decide whether the following statements are true or false. Write *T* on the line if the statement is true. If the statement is false, change the statement to make it true. Cross out the incorrect word or phrase in the sentence. Then, if necessary, write the correct word or phrase on the line.

1. Bill Cosby is a TV star, a writer, and a parent.   _____

2. Distractions make it hard to concentrate on your reading.   _____

3. You should always read with a good light.   _____

4. You should never preview before reading a book.   _____

5. Newspapers and magazines are considered light reading.   _____

6. Skimming is good for heavy reading.   _____

7. Skimming gives you the whole idea of what you're reading.   _____

8. Skimming allows you to read something in half the time.   _____

9. Clustering is not good for reading schoolwork.   _____

10. Clustering takes training and practice.   _____

WHAT'S YOUR OPINION?

1. Learning how to do something new takes time and requires a lot of practice. Why do you think it is worthwhile to spend time learning how to read faster?

_____

_____

_____

_____

2. There are some things such as contracts, poems, or plays, which should not be read quickly. Why do you think it is important to read certain things slowly and carefully?

_____

_____

_____

_____

DEVELOPING SPELLING SKILLS

Study List

admitted
committed
compelled
consulted
controllable
equipped
handicapped
occurred
permitted
previewing
recommendation
referred
revealed
suggestion
transferred

Rule: **When a word ends with a single consonant preceded by a single vowel, double the consonant before adding a suffix that begins with a vowel.**

Examples: **admit + ed** = *admitted*   **admit + ing** = *admitting*
skim + ed = *skimmed*   **skim + ing** = *skimming*
refer + ed = *referred*   **refer + ing** = *referring*

Rule: **When a word ends with two consonants, do *not* double the final consonant when adding a suffix that begins with a vowel.**

Examples: **recommend + ed** = *recommended*
recommend + ing = *recommending*

consult + ed = *consulted*
consult + ing = *consulting*

Rule: **When a word ends with a single consonant that is preceded by two vowels, do *not* double the final consonant when adding a suffix that begins with a vowel.**

Examples: **preview + ed** = *previewed*
preview + ing = *previewing*

reveal + ed = *revealed*
reveal + ing = *revealing*

There are exceptions to most spelling rules. The rules should serve only as general guides. For example, the word *equipped* is an exception. The final consonant is doubled even though it is preceded by two vowels. With a solid knowledge of these Study List words, you will be well equipped to spell similar words without any errors.

SKILL DRILL 1

Write the following Study List words on the lines provided. Then circle the suffix in each word.

1. permitted _____
2. suggestion _____
3. referred _____
4. admitted _____
5. compelled _____
6. occurred _____
7. controllable _____

8. transferred _____
9. revealed _____
10. handicapped _____
11. committed _____
12. equipped _____
13. previewing _____
14. consulted _____

15. recommendation _____

SKILL DRILL 2

The following are short definitions of words from the Study List. Fill the blanks with words from the Study List that match the definitions. If you need help, check the Mini-Dictionary in the back of this book.

1. Disadvantaged in some way _____
2. Able to be controlled _____
3. Asked for information or advice _____
4. Forced to do something _____
5. Devoted to a cause _____
6. Provided with all that is needed _____
7. Confessed that something was true _____
8. Moved something from one place to another _____
9. Something that is suggested _____
10. Happened or took place _____
11. Allowed or gave permission _____
12. Made a secret known _____
13. Looking at something beforehand _____
14. Something that is recommended _____
15. Directed attention to something _____

SKILL DRILL 3

Add the suffix to the base word to form words from the Study List. Write your answers on the line provided.

1. occur + ed = _____
2. equip + ed = _____
3. refer + ed = _____
4. consult + ed = _____
5. commit + ed = _____
6. transfer + ed = _____
7. reveal + ed = _____

8. handicap + ed = _____
9. preview + ing = _____
10. control + able = _____
11. compel + ed = _____
12. admit + ed = _____
13. suggest + ion = _____
14. permit + ed = _____

15. recommend + ation = _____

SKILL DRILL 4

Fill in the charts below by writing each Study List word in its base form, its *ed* form, or its *ing* form.

Base	ed	ing
preview		
	permitted	
		suggesting
refer		
	occurred	
		handicapping
admit		
	committed	
		controlling
compel		
	consulted	
		revealing
transfer		
	recommended	
		equipping

WORD GAME 4

This is a puzzle without clues! Study the length and spelling of each Study List word. Then figure out which words from the Study List fit in the spaces. Once you have found the first word, the rest will be easy to find. Some of the letters are given to you.

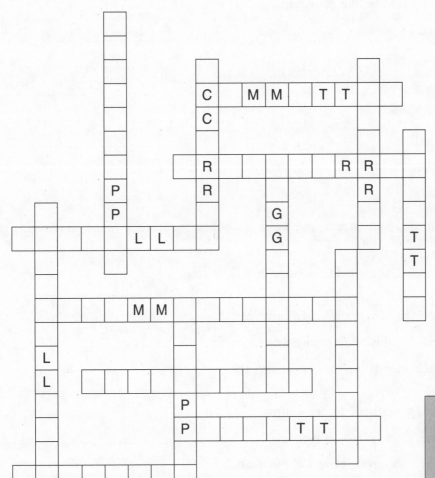

Study List

admitted
committed
compelled
consulted
controllable
equipped
handicapped
occurred
permitted
previewing
recommendation
referred
revealed
suggestion
transferred

HOW WELL CAN YOU SPELL?

Try to take this practice test without looking back at Lesson 4. After you have finished, check your work against the Study List. Correct any mistakes you have made.

A. One word in each of the following pairs of words is spelled incorrectly. Circle that word and spell in correctly on the line provided.

1. permited, admitted   _____

2. occurred, commited   _____

3. compeled, consulted   _____

4. equipped, controlable   _____

5. handicaped, referred   _____

6. previewing, revealled   _____

7. transfered, suggestion   _____

B. In each of the following sentences, one word is spelled incorrectly. Find that word. Then spell it correctly on the line provided.

8. Jake consultted the dictionary before writing his answer.   _____

9. The officer admited that the arrest was a mistake.   _____

10. We will be previewwing this book before we read it.   _____

11. Diana made the reccomendation that we attend the meeting.   _____

12. Mrs. Watson refered a neighbor to her dentist.   _____

13. It was Doug's sugestion to play this record.   _____

14. The accident occured at aprproximately three o'clock.   _____

15. Our laboratory is not equiped for that kind of experiment.   _____

CHALLENGE WORDS

Use what you have learned in this lesson to help you remember how to spell the Challenge Words below.

conferred	excelling	regretted
deterred	unforgettable	propelled
rebelled	emitting	remitting

What Goes Up

Can you scramble an egg? If so, you're more than qualified to juggle. It's that easy. At least that's what they claim in a little book called *Juggling for the Complete Klutz*. It offers a course that simplifies the art and sport of juggling. From the way that juggling has grown in popularity, it seems that juggling fever is easy to catch. There are over one million jugglers in North America alone. Bowling balls, beanbags, hats, swords, clubs, even flaming torches—just name it and someone will find a way to juggle it. There's always a new challenge, and the current world record of juggling 11 objects at a time is waiting to be broken.

Some folks think juggling is just a joke. In a way, they're right. The word *juggle* comes from the Latin word *joculari*. It means "to joke." Historians are not exactly sure when all this catching and tossing began. They do know, however, that it was a popular form of entertainment in the Middle Ages. Court jesters could often be found hurling objects into the air to the delight of the king. During his travels, Marco Polo watched jugglers in Asia. And hundreds of years later, the famous explorer Captain James Cook saw women on the Pacific island of Tonga juggling five gourds at a time! (Tongan women still practice this ancient art.) The oldest record of jugglers is on the wall of an 4,000-year-old Egyptian tomb in a painting that shows four women juggling.

The easiest form of juggling is called the "cascade pattern." The juggler tosses three objects in a pattern that looks like a figure eight turned on its side. Beginners can often learn this pattern in less than an hour. There is no sense in hurrying or rushing, because the key to success is practice—and more practice. But the rewards are worth the effort. Juggling develops both coordination and concentration. One juggler was asked how long it takes to learn a certain trick. "It could take five minutes, or five months," he replied. "It's sort of a toss-up."

REVIEWING YOUR READING

Circle the letter beside the word or phrase that best completes the sentence.

1. The book *Juggling for the Complete Klutz* claims that learning to juggle is

   a. as easy as baking a pie.
   b. more difficult than frying an egg.
   c. as easy as scrambling an egg.
   d. more difficult than writing a book.

2. In North America, there are

   a. very few jugglers.
   b. over one million jugglers.
   c. one million court jesters.
   d. twenty million jugglers.

3. The word *juggle* comes from

   a. a Latin word.
   b. a Greek word.
   c. an English word.
   d. an Egyptian word.

4. The word *joculari* means to

   a. juggle.
   b. throw.
   c. toss.
   d. joke.

5. Captain James Cook saw

   a. Tongan women juggling gourds.
   b. court jesters and kings.
   c. Tongan men juggling gourds.
   d. Marco Polo's adventures.

6. Jesters could often be found hurling objects into the air. The word *hurling* means

   a. catching.
   b. swinging.
   c. throwing.
   d. joking.

7. You can conclude that juggling

   a. has been popular for thousands of years.
   b. is a new form of entertainment.
   c. is only popular in North America.
   d. cannot be done by children.

8. You can conclude that juggling

   a. does not require practice.
   b. can be very dangerous.
   c. will soon be a forgotten art.
   d. requires a great deal of practice.

FIGURING THE FACTS

Decide whether the following statements are true or false. Write *T* on the line if the statement is true. If the statement is false, change the statement to make it true. Cross out the incorrect word or phrase in the sentence. Then, if necessary, write the correct word or phrase on the line.

1. Beanbags and hats are some of the things people juggle.   _____

2. The first known jugglers were probably Greek.   _____

3. Captain James Cook saw jugglers during his travels.   _____

4. On the Pacific island of Tonga, women juggled gourds.   _____

5. The women of Tonga no longer practice juggling.   _____

6. The oldest record of juggling appears in a painting.   _____

7. Juggling has been around for more than 4,000 years.   _____

8. Beginning jugglers learn the "cascade pattern."   _____

9. Most people can learn to juggle in less than a minute.   _____

10. The world record is juggling 22 objects at once.   _____

WHAT'S YOUR OPINION?

1. People have been entertained by jugglers for centuries. Why do you think they are fascinated by jugglers?

_____

_____

_____

_____

_____

2. Experts claim that juggling develops concentration. How important do you think good concentration is in your daily life?

_____

_____

_____

_____

_____

DEVELOPING SPELLING SKILLS

Rule: **When a word ends in *y* preceded by a consonant, change the *y* to *i* before adding any suffix except *ing*. When a word ends in *y* preceded by a vowel, do *not* change the word before adding a suffix.**

The following words contain a final *y* preceded by a consonant.

Examples:	**ed**	**es**	**ing**
reply	replied	replies	replying
qualify	qualified	qualifies	qualifying
simplify	simplified	simplifies	simplifying
hurry	hurried	hurries	hurrying

Remember: **When a word ends in *y* preceded by a vowel, do *not* change the word before adding a suffix.**

Examples: delay   delayed   delays   delaying

Notice that each word on the Study List ends with a suffix. Use the rule above to help you learn these words.

SKILL DRILL 1

Each of the following words is a different form of the Study List word. Write the correct form of the Study List words on the lines provided.

1. grocery _____
2. library _____
3. reply _____
4. deny _____
5. notify _____
6. dismay _____
7. liquefy _____

8. anniversary _____
9. modify _____
10. qualify _____
11. simplify _____
12. dictionary _____
13. hurry _____
14. portray _____

15. delay _____

SKILL DRILL 2

The following are short definitions of words from the Study List. Fill the blanks with words from the Study List that match the definitions. If you need help, check the Mini-Dictionary in the back of this book.

1. Turning into a liquid _____
2. Yearly celebrations _____
3. Food and supplies _____
4. Gave an answer _____
5. Makes something simpler _____
6. Told or gave notice _____
7. Places where books are kept _____
8. Rushing _____
9. Books where definitions are found _____
10. Acted or impersonated _____
11. Stated that something was not true _____
12. Postponed or put off until a later time _____
13. Greatly troubled _____
14. Having the right qualifications _____
15. Changed in some way _____

SKILL DRILL 3

Add the suffix in parentheses to the base form of the following Study List words. Write the words you have formed on the lines provided.

1. portray (ing) _____
2. dictionary (ies) _____
3. grocery (ies) _____
4. liquefy (ed) _____
5. delay (ing) _____
6. dismay (ed) _____
7. reply (ed) _____

8. simplify (ing) _____
9. hurry (ed) _____
10. modify (ing) _____
11. deny (ing) _____
12. qualify (ing) _____
13. notify (ing) _____
14. library (ies) _____

15. anniversary (ies) _____

SKILL DRILL 4

Fill in the charts below by writing each Study List word in its *ed*, *ing*, or *s* form. Remember the rule for changing *y* to *i*.

	ed	ing	s
delay			delays
dismay	dismayed		
portray		portraying	

	ed	ing	es
deny		denying	
hurry			hurries
liquefy	liquefied		
modify		modifying	
notify			notifies
qualify	qualified		
reply		replying	
simplify			simplifies

WORD GAME 5

The words from the Study List are used in this puzzle. The numbers of the clues match the numbers in the puzzle. Read the clues below. Then write your answers in the puzzle blocks.

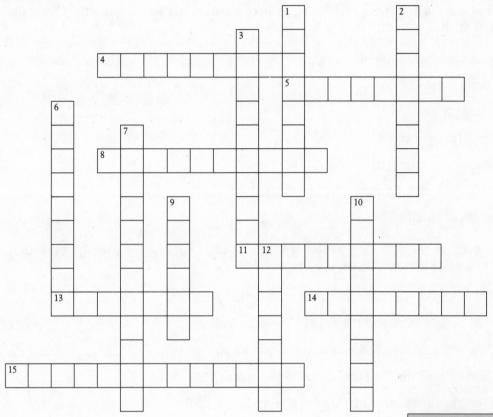

ACROSS

4. Places where you borrow books
5. Changed in some way
8. Makes simpler
11. Food and supplies
13. Postponed or put off until a later time
14. Rushing
15. Yearly celebrations

DOWN

1. Greatly troubled
2. Told or gave notice
3. Turning into liquid
6. Having the right qualifications
7. You look up definitions in them
9. Stated that something is not true
10. Acted or impersonated
12. Gave an answer

Study List

anniversaries
delayed
denied
dictionaries
dismayed
groceries
hurrying
libraries
liquefying
modified
notified
portrayed
qualified
replied
simplifies

HOW WELL CAN YOU SPELL?

Try to take this practice test without looking back at Lesson 5. After you have finished, check your work against the Study List. Correct any mistakes you have made.

A. One word in each of the following pairs of words is spelled incorrectly. Circle that word and spell it correctly on the line provided.

1. anniversaryes, delayed _____

2. simplifiers, hurying _____

3. librarys, denied _____

4. liquefing, groceries _____

5. portrayed, modifyed _____

6. qualifyed, dictionaries _____

7. repliyed, notified _____

B. In each of the following sentences, one word is spelled incorrectly. Find that word. Then spell it correctly on the line provided.

8. We notifyed the police immediately after the accident. _____

9. The actress portraied the famous Egyptian ruler. _____

10. You will find several dictionarys on that shelf. _____

11. Sam denyed that he ever borrowed the ruler. _____

12. The crowd was dismaied by the disappearance of the magician. _____

13. Please put the grocerys on the table. _____

14. Our plane will be delaied about half an hour. _____

15. This little book simplifyes the art of juggling. _____

CHALLENGE WORDS

Use what you have learned in this lesson to help you remember how to spell the Challenge Words below.

falsifying	intensified	specified
symphonies	embassies	verified
signifying	remedies	identities

6

Over Easy

The world's most perfectly designed container is not a Styrofoam cup. Nor is it a gift-wrapped box from a department store. It's an eggshell. It may seem weak and fragile, but it's not. Nature has designed a strong container for the life within a shell. Just place an egg in the center of your palm and squeeze. No amount of pressure will break it. Well, it works most of the time!

Eggs come in a fascinating variety of colors and shapes, not to mention, numerous sizes. The largest egg of any living bird is from the ostrich. Her eggs are about the size of a softball. However, the largest known egg is from an extinct bird that vanished over two thousand years ago. It is called the elephant bird, and its eggs were 14 inches long and 10 inches wide. That's bigger than a basketball! The elephant bird's egg held more than two gallons of liquid. Of course the elephant bird was also as big as an elephant.

Along with roots and berries, eggs were one of the cave man's first foods. Today scientists are looking at eggs as a window to the past. By analyzing ancient specimens, they are learning how to prevent other species from becoming extinct. And by examining shell fragments, they can determine the effect of pesticides and pollution on plant and animal life.

Of course, the eggs we eat most often are from chickens. North America's first chickens were brought here by Christopher Columbus on his second voyage. In fact, the egg you eat for breakfast may well be a gift from a hen whose great, great, great, great grandmother was one of Christopher Columbus' chickens!

Compared to hens 200 years ago, the ones today are "Super Chickens." In the days of Columbus, an average chicken laid only about 12 eggs per year. Today, one chicken produces over 200 eggs a year. That's a lot of yolks!

Speaking of yolks, it is rumored that one of Columbus' hens was worried about the boat trip to the New World. Before leaving, she asked Columbus to make sure that the journey over would be easy. "Over easy?" asked Columbus. "Eggs-actly," answered the chicken.

REVIEWING YOUR READING

Circle the letter beside the word or phrase that best completes the sentence.

1. The largest egg from any living bird is from the

   a. elephant.
   b. chicken.
   c. ostrich.
   d. hen.

2. In addition to eggs, cavemen ate

   a. dinosaurs.
   b. roots and berries.
   c. apples.
   d. other cavemen.

3. Columbus brought chickens to the new world on

   a. the Santa Maria.
   b. his first journey.
   c. the Pinta.
   d. his second journey.

4. Egg shells seem fragile. The word *fragile* most probably means

   a. colorful.
   b. pretty.
   c. delicate.
   d. sturdy.

5. The elephant bird is an extinct species. The word *extinct* most probably means

   a. no longer laying eggs.
   b. existing.
   c. no longer living.
   d. exiting.

6. Scientists are studying eggs to learn more about

   a. the effects of pollution.
   b. the origin of chickens.
   c. the effects of eating chicken.
   d. the origin of the elephant bird.

7. You can conclude that in the days of Columbus, eggs were

   a. plentiful.
   b. an important food supply.
   c. not used on ships.
   d. not available.

8. You can conclude that an eggshell is

   a. a very strong container.
   b. poor protection for the egg.
   c. an indestructible covering.
   d. better than Styrofoam.

FIGURING THE FACTS

Decide whether the following statements are true or false. Write _T_ on the line if the statement is true. If the statement is false, change the statement to make it true. Cross out the incorrect word or phrase in the sentence. Then, if necessary, write the correct word or phrase on the line.

1. Eggs come in different sizes but not shapes. _____

2. The ostrich is the largest living bird to lay eggs. _____

3. The ostrich egg is bigger than a basketball. _____

4. In the time of Columbus chickens laid over 200 eggs a year. _____

5. Man's first food included berries and eggs. _____

6. Today, chickens produce much fewer eggs than 200 years ago. _____

7. An elephant bird's egg contained two gallons of liquid. _____

8. The elephant bird was smaller than an elephant. _____

9. For centuries, the egg has been associated with Easter. _____

10. The elephant bird's egg is the largest ever known. _____

WHAT'S YOUR OPINION?

1. How do you think scientists can protect other species from studying eggs?

_____

_____

_____

_____

_____

2. Why do you think eggs were one of man's first foods?

_____

_____

_____

_____

_____

DEVELOPING SPELLING SKILLS

Study List

acknowledge
aisle
answered
fascinating
foreigner
guarantee
numerous
often
rhyme
rhythm
scenery
scissors
smudge
stomach
tongue

Many words contain letters that you cannot hear when you say the word. Sometimes we call them silent letters. Below are five words from the reading selection that contain silent letters.

guarantee—the *u* is silent
numerous—the *o* is silent

scenery—the *c* is silent
fascinating—the *c* is silent

stomach—the *h* is silent

Because you do not hear these letters when you say the words, it is most important to remember the silent letters when you spell these words.

All the words in the Study List contain silent letters. Memorize the spelling of each, and don't forget the silent letters.

SKILL DRILL 1

Write the following Study List words on the lines provided. Then circle the silent letter or letters in each word.

1. numerous _____
2. foreigner _____
3. fascinating _____
4. tongue _____
5. scissors _____
6. smudge _____
7. answered _____

8. guarantee _____
9. rhyme _____
10. often _____
11. scenery _____
12. rhythm _____
13. aisle _____
14. stomach _____

15. acknowledge _____

SKILL DRILL 2

The following are short definitions of words from the Study List. Fill the blanks with words from the Study List that match the definitions. If you need help, check the Mini-Dictionary in the back of this book.

1. A tool used for cutting _____
2. A visitor from another country _____
3. Part of the body used for speaking _____
4. Part of the body used for digestion _____
5. A smeared stain _____
6. Replied to a question _____
7. Extremely interesting _____
8. Many _____
9. An outdoor view _____
10. The same sound at the end of words or lines of poetry _____
11. Regular repetition of a beat _____
12. A promise to pay or do something _____
13. To express thanks; to admit _____
14. The passage between rows of seats _____
15. Frequent _____

SKILL DRILL 3

Fill the blanks in each of the following words to form words from the Study List. Then write the words you have formed on the line provided.

1. to _ _ ue _____
2. smu _ _ e _____
3. s _ en _ ry _____
4. ac _ _ owle _ ge _____
5. ans _ _ red _____
6. for _ _ g _ er _____
7. g _ _ rant _ _ _____

8. stoma _ _ _____
9. s _ i _ _ ors _____
10. r _ _ t _ m _____
11. a _ sl _ _____
12. o _ _ en _____
13. fas _ _ nating _____
14. numer _ _ s _____

15. r _ _ me _____

SKILL DRILL 4

Answer the following questions by using words from the Study List.

Which words end with *dge*?

1. _____   2. _____

Which words contain the consonant combination *sc*?

3. _____   4. _____

5. _____

Which words begin with *rhy*?

6. _____   7. _____

Which word contains the word *ten*?

8. _____

Which word ends with the consonant combination *ch*?

9. _____

Which word contains the word *reign*?

10. _____

Which word ends with *le*?

11. _____

Which word ends with *ous*?

12. _____

Study List

acknowledge
aisle
answered
fascinating
foreigner
guarantee
numerous
often
rhyme
rhythm
scenery
scissors
smudge
stomach
tongue

Which word ends with *tee*?

13. _____

Which word contains the word *ton*?

14. _____

Which word contains the word *answer*?

15. _____

WORD GAME 6

The words from the Study List are scrambled on the left. Unscramble each word and write it correctly in the spaces on the right. If you unscramble the words correctly, you will find the answer to the puzzle question by reading the shaded column downward. Write your answer on the line below.

HRYHTM

MACHOST

DUGEMS

FTNEO

WEREDSNA

SLAIE

OUSMUNRE

LEDGEKNOWAC

TINGNACISAF

REIGNREFO

EMYHR

YRENECS

SROSSICS

GONTUE

TEENARAUG

What do eggs get in the kitchen? _____

_____

HOW WELL CAN YOU SPELL?

Try to take this practice test without looking back at Lesson 6. After you have finished, check your work against the Study List. Correct any mistakes you have made.

A. One word in each of the following pairs of words is spelled incorrectly. Circle that word and spell it correctly on the line provided.

1. guarantee, numerus   _____

2. ryme, scissors   _____

3. smuge, stomach   _____

4. aisle, aknowledge   _____

5. answered, fasinating   _____

6. foriegner, rhythm   _____

7. scenery, tungue   _____

B. In each of the following sentences, one word is spelled incorrectly. Find that word. Then spell it correctly on the line provided.

8. Robert complained of pains in his stomack.   _____

9. The bride looked lovely as she marched down the isle.   _____

10. Jenny ansered all the questions correctly.   _____

11. We tapped our feet to the rythm of the drums.   _____

12. The senery from our balcony was spectacular.   _____

13. Please be careful with the sharp sissors.   _____

14. A five-year garantee comes with this radio.   _____

15. Ted ofen visits his old school.   _____

CHALLENGE WORDS

Use what you have learned in this lesson to help you remember how to spell the Challenge Words below.

exhibit	guardian	condemn
mortgage	enlighten	adjacent
debtor	doubtful	schedule

Food for Thought

In the eighteenth century, people compared the brain to the wheels and gears of a clock. Today, we compare the brain to a computer. Like computers, the brain works on electrical impulses. But the brain also has chemical reactions. This tiny three-pound mass controls our every thought and deed. The brain is so complex that scientists feel lucky just to be able to describe it. For many researchers, the pursuit of answers to the mysteries of the brain is the last frontier.

Scientists studying the brain have two major goals. First, they need to "map out" the brain. Different parts of the brain control different activities. However, scientists are discovering that certain parts of the brain are connected and work together. For example, one part of the brain may control hearing. But another part allows us to understand what we hear. Researchers think they know which parts of the brain control speech and hearing. But they need to know more about the brain tissues that give us memories, feelings, and thoughts.

The second goal is to understand the *neural code*. This is a "language" that translates what happens outside our bodies into chemical and electrical impulses, which are stored by the brain. When the information is needed later, the brain knows where to find it. The code is carried along by billions of neurons, or cells, which are connected together like circuits. One neuron alone is as intricate as a home computer!

When we eat, we indirectly feed our brain. Food gets into the blood, and blood reaches the brain. Scientists believe that chemicals in certain foods affect our thoughts. Some foods may sharpen our memory or keep us from feeling sad. Researchers think they may be able to isolate these chemicals. This could lead to new ways of treating mental illness. It might even help us improve our ability to learn. If the scientists are correct, the saying "food for thought" may be truer than we think!

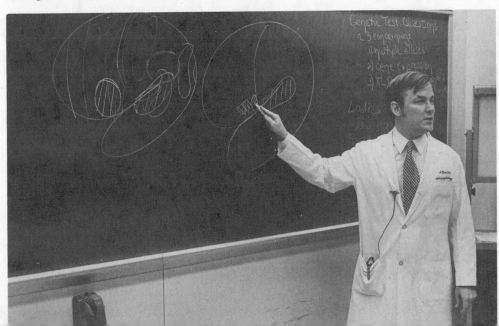

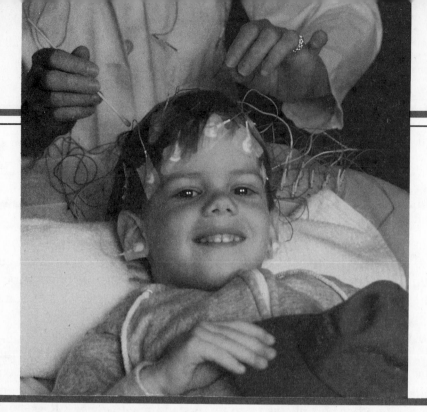

REVIEWING YOUR READING

Circle the letter beside the word or phrase that best completes the sentence.

1. In the eighteenth century, people often compared the brain to

   a. a computer.
   b. a clock.
   c. chemicals.
   d. circuits.

2. Today, we compare the brain to

   a. a chemical clock.
   b. a neuron.
   c. a computer.
   d. an electrical machine.

3. One of the main goals of brain research is to

   a. "map out" the brain.
   b. make an artificial brain.
   c. control memories, thoughts, and feelings.
   d. control speech and hearing.

4. The *neural code* is a type of

   a. brain matter.
   b. tissue.
   c. language.
   d. food.

5. The human brain has billions of

   a. neurons.
   b. foods.
   c. codes.
   d. chemicals.

6. One neuron is as intricate as a home computer. The word *intricate* means

   a. simple.
   b. heavy.
   c. light.
   d. complex.

7. Researchers think they may be able to isolate the chemicals in certain foods. The word *isolate* means

   a. change.
   b. improve.
   c. set apart.
   d. cover up.

8. You can conclude that scientists

   a. are close to finding out how the brain works.
   b. have much more to learn about the brain.
   c. know nothing about the brain.
   d. will soon stop studying the brain.

FIGURING THE FACTS

Decide whether the following statements are true or false. Write _T_ on the line if the statement is true. If the statement is false, change the statement to make it true. Cross out the incorrect word or phrase in the sentence. Then, if necessary, write the correct word or phrase on the line.

1. The brain operates on chemicals as well as electricity.   _____

2. The brain is extremely complex.   _____

3. The brain weighs about ten pounds   _____

4. The neural code translates what happens outside of us and relays it to the brain.   _____

5. When the brain needs information, it knows exactly where it has been stored.   _____

6. One human brain contains billions of neurons.   _____

7. The food we eat gets into our blood.   _____

8. Blood never reaches the human brain.   _____

9. Scientists think some foods may actually help our memory.   _____

10. Scientists are trying to isolate the chemicals in foods that may affect the brain.   _____

WHAT'S YOUR OPINION?

1. Why do we need to learn as much as we can about the human brain?

_____

_____

_____

_____

2. Do you think the foods you eat can affect the way you feel? Why or why not?

_____

_____

_____

_____

_____

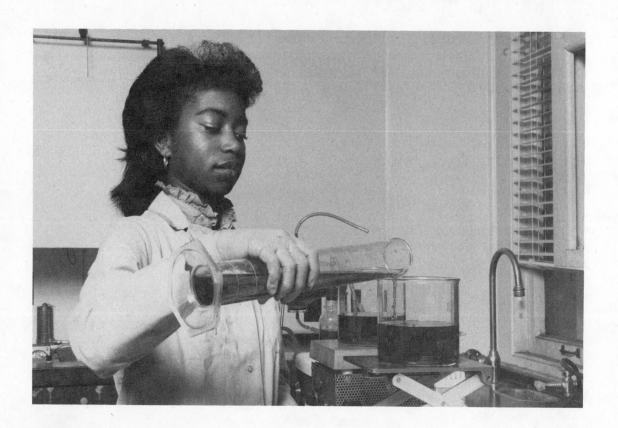

DEVELOPING SPELLING SKILLS

Study List

biscuits
circuit
discontinue
disguise
exquisite
fruitful
guilty
guitar
juiciest
nuisance
pursuit
quilted
rescue
residue
tissue

The following words appear in the reading selection.

pursuit   tissue   circuit

Notice that *pursuit* and *tissue* have similar sounds but are spelled differently.

> *Pursuit* has the *u* sound as in *tube*.
> *Tissue* has the *u* sound as in *tube*.

Notice also that *circuit* and *pursuit* have the same *ui* spelling but are sounded differently.

> *Pursuit* has the *u* sound as in *tube*.
> *Circuit* has the *i* sound as in *sit*.

The vowel combination *ui* is very often confused in spelling because it spells different sounds. The word *disguise* has the *ui* spelling but makes the *i* sound as in *mind*.

As you learn your Study List words, notice these differences in sounds and spellings. This will help you remember the spellings more easily.

SKILL DRILL 1

Write the following Study List words on the lines provided. **Then circle the *ui* or *ue* in each word.**

1. tissue _____
2. pursuit _____
3. guilty _____
4. discontinue _____
5. residue _____
6. nuisance _____
7. fruitful _____

8. rescue _____
9. juiciest _____
10. exquisite _____
11. biscuits _____
12. quilted _____
13. guitar _____
14. disguise _____

15. circuit _____

SKILL DRILL 2

The following are short definitions of words from the Study List. Fill the blanks with words from the Study List that match the definitions. If you need help, check the Mini-Dictionary in the back of this book.

1. The act of chasing someone _____
2. To save someone from danger _____
3. A stringed instrument _____
4. Responsible for doing something wrong _____
5. Plentiful; bearing fruit _____
6. To stop doing something _____
7. A connection of electrical wires _____
8. Cookies or crackers _____
9. A mask or costume _____
10. Extremely beautiful _____
11. The most juicy _____
12. Something that is annoying _____
13. A mass of cells _____
14. What remains after a part is taken _____
15. Sewn together with padding _____

SKILL DRILL 3

Fill the blanks in each of the following words to form words from the Study List. Then write the word you have formed on the line provided.

1. resi _ _ _ _____
2. n _ _ sance _____
3. fr _ _ tful _____
4. discontin _ _ _____
5. c _ rc _ _ t _____
6. g _ _ lty _____
7. p _ _ s _ _ t _____

8. q _ _ lted _____
9. g _ _ tar _____
10. exq _ _ site _____
11. bis _ _ _ ts _____
12. disg _ _ se _____
13. j _ _ ciest _____
14. resc _ _ _____

15. ti _ _ _ _ _____

SKILL DRILL 4

Answer the following questions by using words from the Study List.

Which words spelled with *ue* have the *u* sound as in *tube*?

1. _____ 2. _____
3. _____ 4. _____

Which words spelled with *ui* have the *oo* sound as in *food*?

5. _____ 6. _____
7. _____ 8. _____

Which words spelled with *ui* have the *i* sound as in *sit*?

9. _____ 10. _____
11. _____ 12. _____
13. _____ 14. _____

Which word spelled with *ui* has the *i* sound as in *tie*?

15. _____

WORD GAME 7

The words from the Study List are used in this puzzle. The numbers of the clues match the numbers in the puzzle. Read the clues below. Then write your answers in the puzzle blocks.

ACROSS

2. Responsible for doing something wrong
6. Extremely beautiful
7. Put butter on these
9. To stop doing something
10. Play this as you sing
13. A mass of cells
14. What remains after a part is taken
15. Something that is annoying

DOWN

1. The most juicy
3. Plentiful
4. A costume
5. A connection of electrical wires
8. The act of chasing someone
11. Save from danger
12. Sewn with padding

Study List

biscuits
circuit
discontinue
disguise
exquisite
fruitful
guilty
guitar
juiciest
nuisance
pursuit
quilted
rescue
residue
tissue

HOW WELL CAN YOU SPELL?

Try to take this practice test without looking back at **Lesson 7.** After you have finished, check your work against the Study List. Correct any mistakes you have made.

A. One word in each of the following pairs of words is spelled incorrectly. Circle that word and spell it correctly on the line provided.

1. circut, discontinue   _____

2. exquisite, frootful   _____

3. disguise, persute   _____

4. quillted, tissue   _____

5. residoo, guitar   _____

6. nuisance, reskuoo   _____

7. joociest, guilty   _____

B. In each of the following sentences, one word is spelled incorrectly. Find that word. Then spell it correctly on the line provided.

8. The doctor removed some of the tishoo from the wound.   _____

9. Commuting back and forth to the shop was a noosance.   _____

10. Please play your gitar for us tonight.   _____

11. Joanna felt gilty for not attending the party.   _____

12. That ring is the most exquizite I have ever seen.   _____

13. We will discontinyoo the art class until next term.   _____

14. Jason's disgise was so good, we didn't recognize him.   _____

15. Ann ordered chicken with biskits and gravy for dinner.   _____

CHALLENGE WORDS

Use what you have learned in this lesson to help you remember how to spell the Challenge Words below.

subdue	virtues	suitcases
unsuitable	mannequin	revenue
bruised	avenues	buildings

Tackling Art

"Sports mirrors life perfectly," claims Ernie Barnes. "You get knocked down, and you have to come back—harder." Ernie has a similar feeling about art, and he should, for he is an athlete turned artist. If the transition seems a bit unusual, it is. Mr. Barnes is the first professional football player to cross over from the sports world to the art world.

"I didn't set out to play football," Ernie recalls. "Art was always my first love." While growing up in North Carolina, Ernie had more advantages than other kids in his neighborhood. He lived in a nice home, and there was always plenty of food and clothing. "But I was big, fat, and shy," Ernie says. "I was always the teacher's pet, and I loved to draw. As a result, the other kids teased and made fun of me."

By the time Ernie reached the eighth grade, his size made him a perfect candidate for the football team. "Everyone acted as though it was my responsibility to be on the team. So I tried out, made the team, and then quit." Ernie wasn't used to physical exercise. He was afraid of pushing his body to the limit. But in the ninth grade, Ernie developed a friendship with the school's weightlifting coach. "He told me what I could make of myself, if I really tried," Ernie remembers. "During the rest of high school, I not only played football, I became team captain." At graduation, there were 26 scholarship offers to play football. Ernie selected North Carolina Central University in his home state. There he also studied art.

After college, Ernie played professional football for the San Diego Chargers, and later for the Denver Broncos. His final year in professional football was in the Canadian Football League. Then he decided to become an artist. There was just one problem. How would he support his family? Ernie showed samples of his work to one of the owners of the Chargers. "I told him, 'I want to be the offical artist of the American Football League.'" Ernie got his wish, and a colorful career was born.

Ernie's financial worries soon vanished. Celebrities began buying his paintings, and the art critics praised his work. His Olympic posters were a big hit. It looks as if Ernie Barnes has scored an artistic touchdown.

REVIEWING YOUR READING

Circle the letter beside the word or phrase that best completes the sentence.

1. Today, Ernie Barnes is a

   a. football coach.
   b. sculptor.
   c. painter.
   d. weightlifting coach.

2. According to Ernie Barnes, his "first love" was always

   a. weightlifting.
   b. all kinds of sports.
   c. football.
   d. art.

3. As a child, Ernie was

   a. shy and overweight.
   b. eager to play football.
   c. interested in all sports.
   d. outgoing and friendly.

4. In high school, the other kids

   a. made fun of Ernie.
   b. wanted him to join the football team.
   c. admired his paintings.
   d. elected him president of the student council.

5. Ernie's family

   a. was very poor.
   b. had plenty of food and clothing.
   c. often went without food.
   d. did not have a nice home.

6. Ernie made the transition from football to painting. The word *transition* means

   a. not moving.
   b. changing from one thing to another.
   c. moving in a circle.
   d. remaining in one position.

7. According to the selection, you can conclude that Ernie Barnes is probably

   a. a very small person.
   b. a very large person.
   c. not interested in other sports.
   d. better at football than painting.

8. You can conclude that Ernie became the American Football League's artist because

   a. there was no one else to do the job.
   b. he asked for the job, and his work was good.
   c. the old artist had just been fired.
   d. he had a strong wish for the job.

FIGURING THE FACTS

Decide whether the following statements are true or false. Write *T* on the line if the statement is true. If the statement is false, change the statement to make it true. Cross out the incorrect word or phrase in the sentence. Then, if necessary, write the correct word or phrase on the line.

1. When Ernie was in the eighth grade, he tried out for the football team.   _____

2. Ernie made the team and then quit.   _____

3. Ernie enjoyed physical exercise.   _____

4. Ernie made friends with his high school basketball coach.   _____

5. During high school, Ernie was captain of the football team.   _____

6. When he graduated, he had 26 scholarship offers.   _____

7. The scholarships were for his talent in art.   _____

8. Ernie attended college in his home state.   _____

9. As a professional, Ernie Barnes once played in the Canadian Football League.   _____

10. Ernie Barnes became the official coach of the American Football League.   _____

WHAT'S YOUR OPINION?

1. Ernie's goal was "to be the official artist of the American Football League." Do you think it is important to set goals for yourself? Why?

_____

_____

_____

_____

2. What do you think Ernie meant when he said, "Sports mirrors life perfectly. You get knocked down, and you have to come back—harder"?

_____

_____

_____

_____

DEVELOPING SPELLING SKILLS

Study List

artificial
discussion
financial
friendship
graduation
initial
musician
official
politician
procession
professional
session
special
transition
vanished

In the English language, some sounds are spelled in many different ways. For example, the *sh* sound has several different spellings. The following words are from the reading selection. They contain different spellings of the *sh* sound that are commonly confused.

vanished
friendship   The *sh* sound is spelled *sh*.

financial
official   The *sh* sound is spelled *ci*.

transition
graduation   The *sh* sound is spelled *ti*.

professional   The *sh* sound is spelled *ssi*.

The words in the Study List have different spellings of the *sh* sound. Make sure you take extra care when studying these words. If you memorize them, they will serve as models for other words with similar spellings.

SKILL DRILL 1

Fill the blanks in each of the following words by adding *sh, ci, ti,* or *ssi* to form words from the Study List. Then write the words you have formed on the lines provided.

1. discu _ _ on _____

2. friend _ _ ip _____

3. politi _ _ an _____

4. se _ _ _ on _____

5. artifi _ _ al _____

6. gradua _ _ on _____

7. profe _ _ _ onal _____

8. ini _ _ al _____

9. offi _ _ al _____

10. proce _ _ _ on _____

11. spe _ _ al _____

12. finan _ _ al _____

13. musi _ _ an _____

14. transi _ _ on _____

15. vani _ _ ed _____

SKILL DRILL 2

The following are short definitions of words from the Study List. Fill the blanks with words from the Study List that match the definitions. If you need help, check the Mini-Dictionary in the back of this book.

1. A person who holds a public position _____

2. Disappeared _____

3. A parade; a group of people moving forward _____

4. A person experienced in politics _____

5. Not natural; false _____

6. A conversation or debate _____

7. One who plays a musical instrument _____

8. Distinctive; better than usual _____

9. Having to do with money or finances _____

10. The state of being friends _____

11. The completion of high school or college _____

12. The first or beginning _____

13. A person who is in a certain field of work _____

14. The act of changing from one thing to another _____

15. The term or period of a meeting _____

SKILL DRILL 3

Answer the following questions by using words from the Study List. Write your answers on the lines provided.

Which words spelled with *sh* have the *sh* sound?

1. _____   2. _____

Which words spelled with *ci* have the *sh* sound?

3. _____   4. _____   5. _____

6. _____   7. _____   8. _____

Which words spelled with *ti* have the *sh* sound?

9. _____   10. _____   11. _____

Which words spelled with *ssi* have the *sh* sound?

12. _____   13. _____   14. _____

                        15. _____

SKILL DRILL 4

Answer the following questions by using words from the Study List. Write your answers on the lines provided.

Which words end with the letters *ion*?

1. _____   2. _____

3. _____   4. _____

5. _____

Which words end with the letters *al*?

6. _____   7. _____

8. _____   9. _____

10. _____   11. _____

Which word has the word *ship* in it?

12. _____

Which word has the word *vanish* in it?

13. _____

Which words end with the letters *an*?

14. _____   15. _____

WORD GAME 8

The words from the Study List are scrambled on the left. Unscramble each word and write it correctly in the spaces on the right. If you unscramble the words correctly, you will find the answer to the puzzle question by reading the shaded column downward. Write your answer on the line below.

CILAFNINA

FESSNOIALPRO

CIANTIILOP

NOITISNART

IONDISCSUS

FICIALARTI

CIANMUSI

CIALOFFI

SHEDVANI

LAITINI

ENDFRISHIP

LAICEPS

NOSSIES

ADTIONGRAU

CESSPROION

How could you describe Ernie Barnes?

He's an _____ .

Study List

artificial
discussion
financial
friendship
graduation
initial
musician
official
politician
procession
professional
session
special
transition
vanished

HOW WELL CAN YOU SPELL?

Try to take this practice test without looking back at Lesson 8. After you have finished, check your work against the Study List. Correct any mistakes you have made.

A. One word in each of the following pairs of words is spelled incorrectly. Circle that word and spell it correctly on the line provided.

1. procession, offishal   _____

2. profeshional, initial   _____

3. friendship, artifishal   _____

4. discusshion, musician   _____

5. graduation, polititian   _____

6. seshun, special   _____

7. transishun, financial   _____

B. In each of the following sentences, one word is spelled incorrectly. Find that word. Then spell it correctly on the line provided.

8. The friendssip between these countries is genuine.   _____

9. After graduashun, we will be attending college   _____

10. Club membership requires an inishal fee of three dollars.   _____

11. The crew vanissed as soon as the work was completed.   _____

12. Please pay speshul attention to the instructions.   _____

13. Our cars formed a proceshun that traveled down Main Street.   _____

14. Mrs. Jackson takes care of the company's finantial affairs.   _____

15. Greg wants to be a professional musishian.   _____

CHALLENGE WORDS

Use what you have learned in this lesson to help you remember how to spell the Challenge Words below.

delicious	racial	magician
judicial	quotient	impatient
civilization	application	information

Frozen Secrets

Snowflakes are one of nature's most beautiful mysteries. How do these jewel-like crystals form? Are any two exactly alike? Why are there so many different shapes?

Over the centuries, scientists have had many theories about the formation of snow. To date, however, no one has completely unlocked the secret. The Greek philosopher Aristotle, who lived over 2,000 years ago, had one idea. He said, "When a cloud freezes, there is snow." This is a simple explanation, but it doesn't tell the whole story. It takes extremely cold temperatures for a cloud to freeze. Clouds rarely reach such low temperatures. For snow crystals to form without extreme cold, they must have a "seed." A seed is something solid around which the ice crystal can form. For many years, scientists thought that the seeds were specks of dust. Eventually, they found that this was incorrect. Today, scientists have shown that the seeds for snowflakes come from bacteria. The bacteria come from plants and blow into the oceans. Later, the ocean waves throw the bacteria into the air. This particular type of bacteria contains a molecule that is attracted to the moisture in the clouds. The molecule begins the snow-making process.

Bacteria don't have to be present in every snowflake, however. Once an ice crystal is formed, it multiplies. This process is known as "splintering." As a drop of water freezes, the outside begins to solidify, forming an icy shell. Later, when the inside freezes, it shatters the outside, sending out splinters, like pieces of broken glass. Other crystals form around these splinters. Thus, each splinter becomes the seed for another snowflake.

Although there are many variations, most snowflakes have hexagonal, or six-sided, shapes. That's because the frozen water molecules are six-sided. As the frozen crystals fall to earth, they form arms called *dendrites*. The size and shape of the dendrites depends upon the weather. Because weather changes, the snowflakes that are formed are never quite the same. There's very little chance of finding two snowflakes that are exactly alike.

Scientists are just beginning to solve the mystery of snow. The answers they are finding may help us control the weather someday. There is still a great deal left to uncover. It seems a safe bet that it will be many years before we can melt away these frozen secrets.

REVIEWING YOUR READING

Circle the letter beside the word or phrase that best completes the sentence.

1. Aristotle was

   a. a Roman philosopher.
   b. an ancient ruler.
   c. a Greek philosopher.
   d. a weather forecaster.

2. Aristotle said that snow occurs when

   a. clouds are seeded.
   b. clouds freeze.
   c. temperatures are above normal.
   d. it rains in the north.

3. For a cloud to freeze, it takes

   a. extremely cold temperatures.
   b. many seeds.
   c. extremely high temperatures.
   d. shattering crystals.

4. For many years, scientists thought that the seeds for snow were

   a. frozen clouds.
   b. specks of dust.
   c. frozen atoms.
   d. plant seeds.

5. There are many variations of snowflake shapes. The word *variations* means

   a. slightly different types.
   b. completely different types.
   c. predictable types.
   d. hexagonal types.

6. Snowflakes have hexagonal shapes. The word *hexagonal* means

   a. three-sided.
   b. triangular.
   c. six-sided.
   d. square.

7. You can conclude that the size and shape of snowflakes depends on

   a. weather conditions.
   b. the shape of the seed.
   c. the size of the seed.
   d. temperature only.

8. You can conclude that there is

   a. nothing new to learn about snow.
   b. much more to learn about snow.
   c. very little left to learn about snow.
   d. no reason to study snow today.

FIGURING THE FACTS

Decide whether the following statements are true or false. Write *T* on the line if the statement is true. If the statement is false, change the statement to make it true. Cross out the incorrect word or phrase in the sentence. Then, if necessary, write the correct word or phrase on the line.

1. Aristotle lived over 2,000 years ago. _____

2. For snow crystals to form without extreme cold, they must have a seed. _____

3. Seeds for snowflakes come from bacteria. _____

4. The bacteria for snow comes from the sun. _____

5. The bacteria is thrown into the air by ocean birds. _____

6. This type of bacteria contains a molecule that is attracted to moisture in clouds. _____

7. Bacteria has to be present in every snowflake. _____

8. When a drop of water freezes, it shatters. _____

9. Splinters from frozen drops of water can become seeds for other flakes. _____

10. A *dendrite* is the center of a snowflake. _____

WHAT'S YOUR OPINION?

1. Why do you think snowflakes have fascinated scientists for thousands of years?

_____

_____

_____

_____

_____

2. Why is it important for humankind to unlock the secrets of nature?

_____

_____

_____

_____

_____

DEVELOPING SPELLING SKILLS

Study List

antonym
crystals
cylinder
encyclopedia
gymnasium
hydrogen
hyphen
mysterious
mythology
solidify
symbolic
sympathetic
synonym
synthetic
typhoon

The sound of short *i* as in *hit* and the sound of long *i* as in *kite* are sometimes spelled with a *y*. Look at the following words.

mysteries   crystals   type   solidify

Notice that each of these words has either the short *i* sound or the long *i* sound spelled with a *y*.

Each word in the Study List contains a short or long *i* sound spelled with a *y*. The word *synonym* contains two *y*'s. Each sounds like a short *i*. The word *mythology* also contains a second *y*. But that *y* has the long *e* sound.

SKILL DRILL 1

Write the following Study List words on the lines provided. Then circle all the *y*'s in each word.

1. cylinder _____
2. encyclopedia _____
3. synonym _____
4. synthetic _____
5. mysterious _____
6. hydrogen _____
7. antonym _____

8. crystals _____
9. typhoon _____
10. sympathetic _____
11. solidify _____
12. hyphen _____
13. gymnasium _____
14. mythology _____

15. symbolic _____

SKILL DRILL 2

The following are short definitions of words from the Study List. Fill the blanks with words from the Study List that match the definitions. If you need help, check the Mini-Dictionary in the back of this book.

1. The study of myths or legends _____
2. To harden or become solid _____
3. Having or showing kind feelings toward others _____
4. Clear, transparent minerals that look like ice _____
5. A word that means the opposite of another word _____
6. A word that means the same as another word _____
7. A book or set of books that gives information _____
8. A gas or chemical _____
9. A punctuation mark used to connect parts of a word _____
10. A violent storm; a cyclone _____
11. Artificial _____
12. Used as a symbol of something _____
13. A place where people exercise _____
14. Full of mystery; hard to explain _____
15. A round object with two flat ends, such as a canister _____

▼

SKILL DRILL 3

Fill the blanks in each of the following words to form words from the Study List. Then write the word you have formed on the line provided.

1. t _ ph _ _ n _____

2. s _ non _ m _____

3. s _ mbol _ c _____

4. m _ th _ l _ gy _____

5. h _ ph _ n _____

6. g _ mnas _ _ m _____

7. cr _ stals _____

8. s _ nth _ tic _____

9. s _ mpath _ tic _____

10. solid _ f _ _____

11. m _ ster _ _ us _____

12. h _ drog _ n _____

13. enc _ clo _ _ dia _____

14. c _ l _ nder _____

15. anton _ m _____

▼

SKILL DRILL 4

Answer the following questions by using words from the Study List.

Which words contain the consonant combination *ph*?

1. _____   2. _____

Which words end with *ic*?

3. _____   4. _____

5. _____

Which words end with *ym*?

6. _____   7. _____

Which word contains the word *myth*?

8. _____

Which word contains the word *gym*?

9. _____

Which word contains the word *solid*?

10. _____

Which words contain the consonant combination *cy*?

11. _____   12. _____

Which word ends with the suffix *ious*?

13. _____

Which word begins with the prefix *hydro*?

14. _____

Which word contains the word *cry*?

15. _____

WORD GAME 9

This is a puzzle without clues! Study the length and spelling of each Study List word. Then figure out which words from the Study List fit in the spaces. Once you have found the first word, the rest will be easy to find. Some of the letters are given to you.

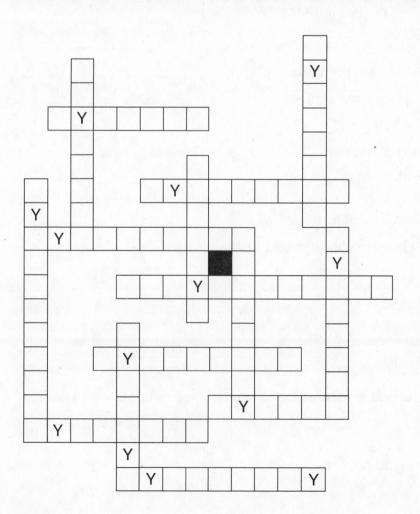

Study List

antonym
crystals
cylinder
encyclopedia
gymnasium
hydrogen
hyphen
mysterious
mythology
solidify
symbolic
sympathetic
synonym
synthetic
typhoon

HOW WELL CAN YOU SPELL?

Try to take this practice test without looking back at Lesson 9. After you have finished, check your work against the Study List. Correct any mistakes you have made.

A. One word in each of the following pairs of words is spelled incorrectly. Circle that word and spell it correctly on the line provided.

1. cilinder, antonym   _____

2. synonym, sinthetic   _____

3. mythology, solidfye   _____

4. hyphen, misterious   _____

5. gimnasium, hydrogen   _____

6. simbolic, sympathetic   _____

7. crystals, ensyclopedia   _____

B. In each of the following sentences, one word is spelled incorrectly. Find that word. Then spell it correctly on the line provided.

8. Zeus is an important figure in Greek mithology.   _____

9. Two words can sometimes be joined by a hifen.   _____

10. Water is made up of hidrogen and oxygen.   _____

11. Dark is an antonim for light.   _____

12. Sunshine is a sinonim for daylight.   _____

13. The teacher was simpathetic to the student's problem.   _____

14. The tiphoon will strike the coastline tomorrow.   _____

15. You will get lemonade by mixing these cristals with water.   _____

CHALLENGE WORDS

Use what you have learned in this lesson to help you remember how to spell the Challenge Words below.

cynical	oxygen	gravity
physician	syllable	pyramids
synopsis	symmetrical	tyranny

Forever Friends

The border between Canada and the United States is the longest undefended border in the world. Both countries share a bond of friendship. And they both share the same continent—North America.

Since most Canadians live within 100 miles of the U.S.-Canadian border, the lives of people in both countries are quite similar. We eat the same foods, listen to the same music, and enjoy the same leisure activities. We also share a common history and geography. As in the U.S., Canada's first inhabitants were Indians. Later, the Vikings, French, and the British came to explore and settle the land. The climate in both countries varies from area to area. And seasonal temperatures change, as they do in many parts of the world.

The U.S. and Canada also share Lake Superior—the largest freshwater lake in the world. This immense body of water is the purest of all the Great Lakes. Both countries are trying to protect it from pollution by establishing national parks on its shores. Although they may succeed in keeping the lake clean, there is little they can do about the temperature of the water. Those who are brave enough to swim there do not stay for long.

Canada is responsible for many significant contributions to science and medicine. These include the invention of the electron microscope and the development of insulin. Both discoveries have greatly improved health conditions in our lifetime. In agriculture, there is the McIntosh apple—the crisp, juicy apple cultivated by John McIntosh, a Canadian. Both Canada and the U.S. can claim credit for the telephone. Alexander Graham Bell, a U.S. citizen, developed the telephone while living in Canada.

In sports, Canada has given the world ice hockey, lacrosse, and basketball. That's right. Basketball was invented by James Naismith—a Canadian. In the entertainment world, a list of famous Canadians would definitely include John Candy, Gordon Lightfoot, Martin Short, Dan Aykroyd, William Shatner, Michael J. Fox, Peter Jennings, and Walt Disney. And the list of famous Canadian entertainers goes on and on.

As you can see, the people of the United States and Canada share many things. But the most important by far is the common bond of friendship.

REVIEWING YOUR READING

Circle the letter beside the word or phrase that best completes the sentence.

1. The border between Canada and the United States is

   a. the world's longest.
   b. the world's longest that is undefended.
   c. separated by a huge wall.
   d. a mountain range.

2. Most Canadians live within

   a. one mile of the border.
   b. 10 miles of the border.
   c. 100 miles of the border.
   d. 1,000 miles of the border.

3. Canada's first inhabitants were

   a. French.
   b. English.
   c. Vikings.
   d. Indians.

4. You can conclude that Lake Superior is

   a. the smallest of the Great Lakes.
   b. polluted.
   c. the cleanest of all the Great Lakes.
   d. warmer than other lakes.

5. The McIntosh apple was first cultivated by a Canadian. The word *cultivated* means

   a. grown.
   b. built.
   c. tested.
   d. tasted.

6. James Naismith was a Canadian who invented

   a. baseball.
   b. lacrosse.
   c. basketball.
   d. ice hockey.

7. You can conclude that life in Canada is

   a. very different from life in the U.S.
   b. very difficult.
   c. easier than life in most other countries.
   d. similar to life in the U.S.

8. You can conclude that the U.S. and Canada

   a. are the same size.
   b. are good neighbors.
   c. have never had formal trade agreements.
   d. have the same form of government.

FIGURING THE FACTS

Decide whether the following statements are true or false. Write _T_ on the line if the statement is true. If the statement is false, change the statement to make it true. Cross out the incorrect word or phrase in the sentence. Then, if necessary, write the correct word or phrase on the line.

1. Canada and the U.S. share a common history and geography.   _____

2. The climate in both countries varies from area to area.   _____

3. The Vikings, French, and British explored Canada.   _____

4. Lake Superior is the smallest freshwater lake in the world.   _____

5. A U.S. citizen invented the electron microscope.   _____

6. Alexander Graham Bell once lived in Canada.   _____

7. The sport of ice hockey was created in the United States.   _____

8. John Candy and Dan Aykroyd are both Canadians.   _____

9. The sport of basketball was invented by a Canadian.   _____

10. Canada and the United States are on two different continents.   _____

WHAT'S YOUR OPINION?

1. Why do you think Canada and the United States are good neighbors?

_____

_____

_____

_____

_____

2. Do you think the United States and Canada will continue to be good friends in the future? Why or why not?

_____

_____

_____

_____

_____

DEVELOPING SPELLING SKILLS

Study List

article
commercial
double
economical
fictional
fragile
missile
personal
receptacle
rehearsal
seasonal
several
simple
spectacle
survival

The following words appear in the reading selection.

national   settle   seasonal   responsible

Notice that these words all end with the same *el* sound, but they are spelled differently. Although there are other ways to spell this sound, the *le* and *al* endings are the most commonly confused.

As you learn the Study List words, pay special attention to the *al* or *le* ending in each word.

SKILL DRILL 1

Write the following Study List words on the lines provided. Then circle the *al* or *le* ending in each word.

1. survival _____

2. simple _____

3. seasonal _____

4. article _____

5. double _____

6. personal _____

7. fragile _____

8. spectacle _____

9. several _____

10. rehearsal _____

11. commercial _____

12. receptacle _____

13. missile _____

14. economical _____

15. fictional _____

SKILL DRILL 2

The following are short definitions of words from the Study List. Fill the blanks with words from the Study List that match the definitions. If you need help, check the Mini-Dictionary in the back of this book.

1. Twice as much _____

2. Easily broken; delicate _____

3. A few _____

4. Not real; made up _____

5. Practice for a play _____

6. Having to do with the seasons _____

7. A very grand display _____

8. A container for storing something _____

9. A rocket that is projected into space _____

10. A certain thing or item _____

11. Having to do with commerce; an advertisement _____

12. Thrifty; not wasteful _____

13. Easy to do or understand _____

14. The act of surviving or lasting _____

15. Private; something individual _____

SKILL DRILL 3

Fill the blanks in each of the following words to form words from the Study List. Then write the words you have formed on the lines provided.

1. fict _ _ n _ _ _____

2. mi _ _ i _ _ _____

3. co _ _ erci _ _ _____

4. se _ _ r _ _ _____

5. fra _ i _ _ _____

6. do _ b _ _ _____

7. s _ _ son _ _ _____

8. econ _ _ ic _ _ _____

9. rec _ _ tac _ _ _____

10. reh _ _ rs _ _ _____

11. spec _ _ c _ _ _____

12. per _ _ n _ _ _____

13. art _ c _ _ _____

14. sim _ _ _ _____

15. sur _ _ v _ _ _____

SKILL DRILL 4

Answer the following questions by using words from the Study List.

Which words end with *ile*?

1. _____   2. _____

Which word ends with *ble*?

3. _____

Which words end with *cle*?

4. _____   5. _____

6. _____

Which word ends with *cial*?

7. _____

Which word ends with *val*?

8. _____

Which word ends with *sal*?

9. _____

Which words end with *nal*?

10. _____   11. _____

12. _____

Study List

article
commercial
double
economical
fictional
fragile
missile
personal
receptacle
rehearsal
seasonal
several
simple
spectacle
survival

Which word ends with *ral*?

13. _____

Which word ends with *ple*?

14. _____

Which word ends with *cal*?

15. _____

WORD GAME 10

The words from the Study List are scrambled on the left. Unscramble each word and write it correctly in the spaces on the right. If you unscramble the words correctly, you will find the answer to the puzzle question by reading the shaded column downward. Write your answer on the line below.

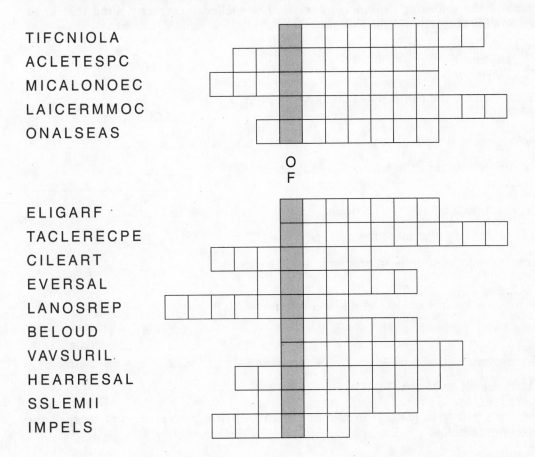

TIFCNIOLA

ACLETESPC

MICALONOEC

LAICERMMOC

ONALSEAS

O
F

ELIGARF

TACLERECPE

CILEART

EVERSAL

LANOSREP

BELOUD

VAVSURIL

HEARRESAL

SSLEMII

IMPELS

How could you describe the border between Canada and the United States?

_____

HOW WELL CAN YOU SPELL?

Try to take this practice test without looking back at Lesson 10. After you have finished, check your work against the Study List. Correct any mistakes you have made.

A. One word in each of the following pairs of words is spelled incorrectly. Circle that word and spell it correctly on the line provided.

1. receptical, rehearsal   _____

2. several, seasonel   _____

3. spectical, simple   _____

4. survivel, article   _____

5. commercial, doubel   _____

6. economical, fictionel   _____

7. missel, fragile   _____

B. In each of the following sentences, one word is spelled incorrectly. Find that word. Then spell it correctly on the line provided.

8. Paul clipped the artical about baseball out of the newspaper.   _____

9. We watched for the commershel on television, but missed it.   _____

10. There are severil roads that you can take to get there.   _____

11. The first rehearsel of the school play will be on Thursday.   _____

12. She sent a personel note to her friend.   _____

13. Mr. Wilkins forgot to mark the package "fragil."   _____

14. Using leftovers in soup is an economicel way to save money.   _____

15. Instructions for this model should be quite simpel.   _____

CHALLENGE WORDS

Use what you have learned in this lesson to help you remember how to spell the Challenge Words below.

assemble	crumble	axle
mammal	visual	mutual
resemble	influential	confidential

Run for Life

"I wanted to show that people like me are physically challenged, not handicapped," Jeff Keith said. He was referring to his courageous run across the United States. "Handicapped is too negative a word," Jeff explained. "This run was for all the people in hospitals and rehabilitation centers. For anyone confined. It was to show that they can overcome their disabilities."

Running a total of 3,300 miles is amazing enough. But what makes it even more incredible is the fact that Jeff has a 6-pound plastic leg with an artificial foot. For 8 months, Jeff sprinted 12 miles each day. He and the few friends who accompanied him braved rain, snow, heat, and even tornado watches. When the run was completed, Jeff had worn out 36 pairs of sneakers!

Few people thought that Jeff would be able to complete the journey. "There were a lot of doubters," Jeff said. Even his mother questioned such a far-fetched idea. "Jeff called me up the day he was going to begin," she said. "He asked, 'Mom, which bag did you pack my sneakers in?' I thought, 'And he's going to run 3,300 miles?'" But Jeff knew he could do it. He was well prepared for the challenge. At age 12, he had lost his leg due to a cancer operation. But that loss never held him back. He became a lacrosse player and a skier. He even finished a competition that required swimming, bicycling, and running.

Jeff's run, which began in Boston, was sponsored by the American Cancer Society. By the time Jeff completed the trek in Los Angeles, he had raised over $120,000 in contributions. Jeff had been inspired by Terry Fox, who had also lost a leg to cancer. Terry had tried to jog across Canada. He made it two-thirds of the way before illness stopped him.

What's next? Of course, there will be more skiing and athletic competitions. "Who knows?" Jeff says. "I may just swim the English Channel!"

REVIEWING YOUR READING

Circle the letter beside the word or phrase that best completes the sentence.

1. Jeff Keith believes that physically handicapped people are

   a. physically challenged.
   b. physically unable.
   c. not good athletes.
   d. superior runners.

2. Jeff's journey was across

   a. Canada.
   b. South America.
   c. the United States.
   d. Los Angeles.

3. Jeff's run was sponsored by

   a. his friends.
   b. the Terry Fox Foundation.
   c. the American Cancer Society.
   d. hospitals and rehabilitation centers.

4. At age 12, Jeff

   a. ran across Canada.
   b. lost his leg to cancer.
   c. won a bicycle race.
   d. was hit by an automobile.

5. Jeff's run was inspired by Terry Fox. The word *inspired* means

   a. sponsored.
   b. completed.
   c. planned.
   d. influenced or caused.

6. You can conclude that Jeff's mother

   a. asked Jeff to make the run.
   b. was displeased that he had made it.
   c. had doubts about Jeff's success.
   d. ran along with Jeff.

7. Jeff's trek was completed in Los Angeles. The word *trek* means a

   a. very short walk.
   b. long journey.
   c. special race.
   d. railroad's end.

8. You can conclude that after Jeff lost his leg, he

   a. kept facing new challenges.
   b. was afraid to try new things.
   c. decided to attend college.
   d. never went skiing again.

FIGURING THE FACTS

Decide whether the following statements are true or false. Write *T* on the line if the statement is true. If the statement is false, change the statement to make it true. Cross out the incorrect word or phrase in the sentence. Then, if necessary, write the correct word or phrase on the line.

1. Jeff's run was longer than 5,000 miles.   _____

2. Jeff has a 6-pound plastic leg.   _____

3. He also has an artifical foot.   _____

4. Jeff made his journey completely alone.   _____

5. During the journey, Jeff wore out 50 pairs of sneakers.   _____

6. Terry Fox tried to run across the United States.   _____

7. Jeff's run began in Los Angeles.   _____

8. Jeff raised over $120,000 for the American Cancer Society.   _____

9. There were a lot of people who doubted Jeff could make it.   _____

10. Jeff lost his leg to a cancer operation.   _____

WHAT'S YOUR OPINION?

1. What do you think Jeff Keith means when he says, "Handicapped is too negative a word"?

   _____

   _____

   _____

   _____

2. Jeff has said, "We all can make a difference in the world today." Do you agree with him? How can we make a difference?

   _____

   _____

   _____

   _____

DEVELOPING SPELLING SKILLS

Study List

acceptable
accompany
accuse
committee
competition
completed
confirm
conjunction
contribution
disabilities
dispute
dissolve
recommend
recreation
required

The following words appear in the reading selection.

contributions   completed   disabilities
accompanied   required

All of these words begin with prefixes. A *prefix* is a word part that is added to the beginning of a word or the root of a word. Each prefix has its own meaning.

com
con } mean *with* or *together*

dis   means *not*
ac   means *to* or *toward*
re   means *back* or *again*

A prefix may be added to the base of a word to change the meaning of the whole word.

Example: **dis** + **ability** = *disability*

Notice that each word in the Study List begins with a prefix.

SKILL DRILL 1

Write the following Study List words on the lines provided. Then draw a line between the prefix and the root in each word.

1. completed _____

2. dispute _____

3. acceptable _____

4. confirm _____

5. recreation _____

6. accompany _____

7. committee _____

8. disabilities _____

9. required _____

10. accuse _____

11. conjunction _____

12. recommend _____

13. contribution _____

14. competition _____

15. dissolve _____

SKILL DRILL 2

The following are short definitions of words from the Study List. Fill the blanks with words from the Study List that match the definitions. If you need help, check the Mini-Dictionary in the back of this book.

1. Play or amusement _____

2. Needed or demanded _____

3. To give a suggestion _____

4. To go along with someone _____

5. To blame _____

6. Worth accepting _____

7. An argument or discussion _____

8. Physical conditions that disable _____

9. To make into a liquid _____

10. A connecting word _____

11. A gift or donation, usually money _____

12. A group of people who decide something _____

13. A type of athletic event _____

14. Finished _____

15. To prove something to be true or correct _____

SKILL DRILL 3

Fill the blanks in each of the following words to form words from the Study List. Then write the word you have formed on the line provided.

1. co _ _ i _ _ ee _____

2. comp _ _ it _ _ n _____

3. co _ _ ribu _ _ on _____

4. re _ _ ired _____

5. reco _ _ end _____

6. disp _ _ e _____

7. ac _ _ pt _ _ le _____

8. compl _ _ _ d _____

9. conjun _ _ ion _____

10. conf _ _ m _____

11. recr _ _ tion _____

12. di _ _ olve _____

13. disabil _ _ ies _____

14. a _ _ use _____

15. a _ _ ompany _____

SKILL DRILL 4

Answer the following questions by using words from the Study List.

Which words begin with the prefixes that means *with* or *together*?

1. _____   2. _____

3. _____   4. _____

5. _____   6. _____

Which words begin with the prefix that means *back* or *again*?

7. _____   8. _____

9. _____

Which words begin with the prefix that means *not*?

10. _____   11. _____

12. _____

Which words begin with the prefix that means *to* or *toward*?

13. _____   14. _____

15. _____

WORD GAME 11

Use the words from the Study List to complete this crossword puzzle.

ACROSS

1. Needed or demanded
2. To blame
5. A group of people who decide something
6. To give a suggestion
8. An argument
11. Worth accepting
12. A gift or donation
13. To prove something true or correct

DOWN

1. Play or amusement
3. Finished
4. A connecting word
7. To make liquid
8. Physical conditions that disable
9. A type of athletic event
10. To go along with someone

Study List

acceptable
accompany
accuse
committee
competition
completed
confirm
conjunction
contribution
disabilities
dispute
dissolve
recommend
recreation
required

HOW WELL CAN YOU SPELL?

Try to take this practice test without looking back at **Lesson 11.** After you have finished, check your work against the Study List. Correct any mistakes you have made.

A. One word in each of the following pairs of words is spelled incorrectly. Circle that word and spell it correctly on the line provided.

1. acceptible, required _____

2. recreaytion, confirm _____

3. acompany, committee _____

4. completed, acuse _____

5. contribution, congunction _____

6. disolve, dispute _____

7. competitshun, recommend _____

B. In each of the following sentences, one word is spelled incorrectly. Find that word. Then spell it correctly on the line provided.

8. Jeff believes that handicaps are not dissabilities. _____

9. A jacket is recwired while you are in the restaurant. _____

10. Mr. Foster was quick to recomend the course on Shakespeare. _____

11. The disput was between the leaders of the two countries. _____

12. Our class project will be compleeted by tonight. _____

13. Manuel is head of the commitee for student government. _____

14. Maria will conferm the fact that I was at the meeting. _____

15. Our club's contribushun was quite large. _____

CHALLENGE WORDS

Use what you have learned in this lesson to help you remember how to spell the Challenge Words below.

confined	distribute	reproduce
accommodate	comparison	complaint
consideration	convenience	refreshment

The Wall

If you were to walk across the green grass of the Washington Mall in Washington D.C., you would see an unexpected sight. A slash of shiny black stone cuts its way into the landscape. It is the Vietnam Veterans Memorial. The design is quite simple and yet breathtakingly beautiful. Two polished granite walls, growing increasingly larger, meet to form a "V" shape. Engraved in the stone are names. There are 58,007 of them. They are the names of the men and women who died or were reported missing during the Vietnam War. You cannot help reaching out and touching the names of friends and relatives. When you do, your hand is reflected in the polished granite. It is almost as if another hand is reaching out from within. Visitors to the monument have said that it inspires tears and quiet contemplation.

This emotionally stirring sculpture was designed by architect Maya Ying Lin. She drew the plans for it while studying at Yale University. Maya submitted her model as part of a national competition. The idea of the contest was to create a tribute to those lost in Vietnam. Participants were asked to design a memorial that would inspire thought and reflection. Maya's design was unanimously chosen. All the judges voted for it.

The wall took several years to complete. Vietnam veterans raised the funds to pay for it. The memorial was dedicated on Veterans Day, or Remembrance Day as it is called in Canada. At the dedication, one speaker said, "A nation that forgets the sacrifices of its heroes risks its very existence." Maya Ying Lin's sculpture makes it impossible to forget. As President Ronald Reagan said, "This memorial is a symbol of both past and current sacrifice."

REVIEWING YOUR READING

Circle the letter beside the word or phrase that best completes the sentence.

1. The Vietnam Veterans Memorial is made of

   a. black marble.
   b. gray granite.
   c. black granite.
   d. green marble.

2. The walls of the memorial meet to form

   a. a "V" shape.
   b. an "X" shape.
   c. two hills.
   d. a statue.

3. The walls of the memorial are engraved with

   a. dates.
   b. poetry.
   c. names.
   d. designs.

4. Maya Ying Lin

   a. built the monument.
   b. engraved the stone.
   c. paid for the memorial.
   d. designed the memorial.

5. Maya Ying Lin's work was chosen

   a. as part of a competition.
   b. because she was a veteran.
   c. as part of her schoolwork.
   d. because she was an architect.

6. Maya's design ws unanimously chosen. The word *unanimously* means

   a. everyone voted for it.
   b. only a few people voted for it.
   c. chosen by mistake.
   d. chosen by chance.

7. The memorial is a symbol of both past and current sacrifice. The word *current* means

   a. happening yesterday.
   b. happening today.
   c. taking place in the past.
   d. not in the present.

8. The memorial inspires quiet contemplation. The word *contemplation* means

   a. discussion.
   b. argument.
   c. thinking to oneself.
   d. crying.

FIGURING THE FACTS

Decide whether the following statements are true or false. Write *T* on the line if the statement is true. If the statement is false, change the statement to make it true. Cross out the incorrect word or phrase in the sentence. Then, if necessary, write the correct word or phrase on the line.

1. The Vietnam Veterans Memorial is in New York. _____

2. The memorial's stone walls grow increasingly larger. _____

3. There are 58,007 names engraved in the wall. _____

4. The names are of those who built the monument. _____

5. You can see your hand reflected in the polished granite. _____

6. Maya Ying Lin is an architect. _____

7. She created the design while she was in high school. _____

8. The wall took many years to complete. _____

9. In Canada, Veterans Day is called Remembrance Day. _____

10. Vietnam veterans raised funds to build the monument. _____

WHAT'S YOUR OPINION?

1. What kind of sacrifice was President Reagan speaking of when he said, "This memorial is a symbol of both past and current sacrifice"?

_____

_____

_____

_____

_____

2. Why do you think it is important for a nation to remember its heroes?

_____

_____

_____

_____

_____

DEVELOPING SPELLING SKILLS

Study List

engraved
enthusiasm
environment
inconvenient
increasingly
inspiring
reflection
respiration
responsibility
submitted
substitution
subterranean
unexpected
unnecessary
unsatisfactory

The following words appear in the reading selection. Each word begins with a prefix.

| *unexpected* | *increasingly* | *engraved* |
| *reflected* | | *submitted* |

Remember: **A *prefix* is a word part that is added to the beginning of a word or a root. Each prefix has its own meaning.**

un   means *not*
in   means *not, in,* or *cause to be*
en   means *in, make,* or *cause to be*
re   means *back* or *again*
sub   means *under* or *below*

Knowing the meanings of various prefixes can help you determine the meaning of an unfamiliar word. Many words are made up of a prefix and a base. If you know the meaning of a prefix and the meaning of a base, you can sometimes figure out the meaning of a whole word.

Example: **un** = *not*   **necessary** = *needed*
          unnecessary = *not needed*

Notice that each word in the Study List begins with a prefix.

SKILL DRILL 1

Write the following Study List words on the lines provided. Then draw a line between the prefix and the root in each word.

1. subterranean _____
2. engraved _____
3. unsatisfactory _____
4. submitted _____
5. responsibility _____
6. respiration _____
7. increasingly _____

8. unexpected _____
9. enthusiasm _____
10. environment _____
11. reflection _____
12. substitution _____
13. inspiring _____
14. unnecessary _____

15. inconvenient _____

SKILL DRILL 2

The following are short definitions of words from the Study List. Fill the blanks with words from the Study List that match the definitions. If you need help, check the Mini-Dictionary in the back of this book.

1. Happening more and more _____

2. The world around you; your surroundings _____

3. Excitement or strong interest _____

4. Not convenient _____

5. The act of putting one thing in place of another _____

6. Underground _____

7. Not expected; surprising _____

8. Not really needed _____

9. Not good enough to satisfy _____

10. The act of breathing _____

11. Carved into something _____

12. An image in a mirror; serious thought _____

13. Offered for consideration _____

14. Affecting one's emotions; influencing or causing _____

15. Duty or obligation _____

SKILL DRILL 3

Fill the blanks in each of the following words to form words from the Study List. Then write the word you have formed on the line provided.

1. respon _ _ bi _ _ ty _____

2. submi _ _ ed _____

3. unsatis _ _ ct _ _ y _____

4. engr _ _ ed _____

5. incon _ _ n _ _ nt _____

6. insp _ _ ing _____

7. subte _ _ an _ _ n _____

8. resp _ _ at _ _ n _____

9. subs _ _ tu _ _ on _____

10. un _ _ ce _ _ ary _____

11. enthu _ _ a _ _ _____

12. incr _ _ singly _____

13. unex _ _ cted _____

14. envi _ _ _ ment _____

15. refl _ _ t _ _ n _____

SKILL DRILL 4

Answer the following questions by using words from the Study List.

Which words begin with the prefix that means *not, in,* or *cause to be*?

1. _____   2. _____

3. _____

Which words begin with the prefix that only means *not*?

4. _____   5. _____

6. _____

Which words begin with the prefix that means *in, make,* or *cause to be*?

7. _____   8. _____

9. _____

Which words begin with the prefix that means *back* or *again*?

10. _____   11. _____

12. _____

Which words begin with the prefix that means *under* or *below*?

13. _____   14. _____

15. _____

WORD GAME 12

This is a puzzle without clues! Study the length and spelling of each Study List word. Then figure out which words from the Study List fit in the spaces. Once you have found the first word, the rest will be easy to find. Some of the letters are given to you.

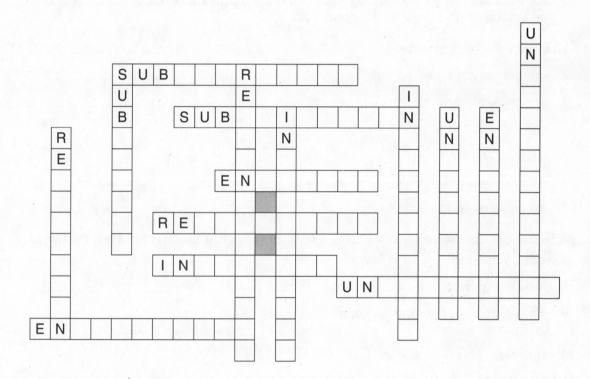

Study List

engraved
enthusiasm
environment
inconvenient
increasingly
inspiring
reflection
respiration
responsibility
submitted
substitution
subterranean
unexpected
unnecessary
unsatisfactory

HOW WELL CAN YOU SPELL?

Try to take this practice test without looking back at Lesson 12. After you have finished, check your work against the Study List. Correct any mistakes you have made.

A. One word in each of the following pairs of words is spelled incorrectly. Circle that word and spell it correctly on the line provided.

1. responsibility, resperation   _____

2. submitted, substitooshun   _____

3. unexpeckted, environment   _____

4. engraved, enthusiasem   _____

5. inspiring, unsatisfactery   _____

6. reflectshun, inconvenient   _____

7. unnecessary, increesingly   _____

B. In each of the following sentences, one word is spelled incorrectly. Find that word. Then spell it correctly on the line provided.

8. Maya submited her design to the council for approval.   _____

9. The dance tickets are the responsability of the committee.   _____

10. Our parking space was quite inconvenyent.   _____

11. We must protect our enviroment if we wish to survive.   _____

12. The mess they made was unecessary.   _____

13. Shirley's locket was ingraved with her initials.   _____

14. The class found the play enspiring and entertaining.   _____

15. The prisoners escaped through a subteranean tunnel.   _____

CHALLENGE WORDS

Use what you have learned in this lesson to help you remember how to spell the Challenge Words below.

unyielding	enchanting	resources
unquestionable	substantial	enlargement
revolutionary	involuntary	encounter

13

Pulling Her Weight

There are those who claim that bodybuilding is not a sport. Lydia Cheng does not agree. She says, "I think that any physical endeavor that involves a goal that you want to attain with your body is a sport." Lydia should know. She is a professional bodybuilder.

Lydia has been serious about bodybuilding for a number of years. At the suggestion of her husband-to-be, she went to the Columbia University weight room. "It was kind of a scruffy place," she said. "Guys looked at me and said, 'Step aside, lady, and wait till we're finished.'" At that time, Lydia let nervousness get the better of her, and she stepped aside. But she doesn't step aside anymore! After a few years of training, Lydia entered the East Coast Bodybuilding Championships. She came in first in the women's division. Later, she entered various other competitions and won several of them. Finally, Lydia decided to turn professional. Her most important competition so far has been the Ms. Olympia contest in Montreal. She did not win a prize. But just being chosen for the competition was a tremendous achievement.

Bodybuilding is the art of shaping muscles. It is not just lifting weights to gain strength. A large part of competitive bodybuilding includes posing. This requires movements set to music and performed before an audience. Each routine takes planning, rehearsing, skill, and concentration. There was a time when bodybuilding for women was unheard of. Previously, men had dominated the bodybuilding arena. But today, more and more bodybuilders are welcoming women into the gym.

Aside from working out, Lydia finds time for a few of her other interests. She is a part-time model and trains people in physical fitness. Lydia is also studying for her master's degree in French. It's a subject she should be well prepared for. Her mother is French Canadian.

Lydia smiles, remembering the time she offered to help a man move a large TV set. "A woman can't lift that. It's too heavy," the man insisted. Lydia just grinned, bent over, and picked up the other end of the set.

REVIEWING YOUR READING

Circle the letter beside the word or phrase that best completes the sentence.

1. Lydia Cheng is

   a. an amateur bodybuilder.
   b. a professional bodybuilder.
   c. an amateur French teacher.
   d. a professional entertainer.

2. The first time Lydia tried lifting weights was at a

   a. high school gym.
   b. girl's club.
   c. university's weight room.
   d. neighborhood gym.

3. Lifting weights was suggested to Lydia by her

   a. mother.
   b. coach.
   c. neighbor.
   d. husband-to-be.

4. Lydia began to enter competitions after

   a. a few days of training.
   b. gaining 20 pounds.
   c. a few years of training.
   d. losing 20 pounds.

5. According to Lydia, any physical endeavor that involves a goal is a sport. The word *endeavor* means

   a. effort.
   b. motion.
   c. craft.
   d. job.

6. You can conclude that the first time Lydia went to a weight room

   a. the men welcomed her.
   b. she was not at all nervous.
   c. she met her husband-to-be.
   d. she was quite nervous.

7. You can conclude that some years ago there were

   a. more female than male bodybuilders.
   b. no women allowed in gyms.
   c. few female bodybuilders.
   d. few male bodybuilders.

8. Previously, men had dominated the bodybuilding arena. The word *dominated* means

   a. designed.
   b. controlled.
   c. supported.
   d. encouraged.

FIGURING THE FACTS

Decide whether the following statements are true or false. Write *T* on the line if the statement is true. If the statement is false, change the statement to make it true. Cross out the incorrect word or phrase in the sentence. Then, if necessary, write the correct word or phrase on the line.

1. Lydia has been bodybuilding for a year.   _____

2. In her first competition, Lydia came in last.   _____

3. Lydia did not win a prize in Montreal.   _____

4. Bodybuilding is the art of shaping muscles.   _____

5. Part of a bodybuilding competition includes
   movements set to music.   _____

6. Lydia is studying for her master's degree in English.   _____

7. Lydia's mother is French Canadian.   _____

8. Lydia works as a full-time model.   _____

9. Lydia also trains people in physical fitness.   _____

10. Today, male bodybuilders are welcoming female
    bodybuilders into weight rooms.   _____

WHAT'S YOUR OPINION?

1. Lydia says that "any physical endeavor that involves a goal that you want to attain with your body is a sport." Do you agree with her definition of a sport? Explain why or why not.

   _____

   _____

   _____

   _____

   _____

2. Why do you think bodybuilding for women was unheard of in the past? Why do you think women are interested in bodybuilding today?

   _____

   _____

   _____

   _____

   _____

DEVELOPING SPELLING SKILLS

Study List
courteously
enormousness
envious
miscellaneous
nervousness
precious
previously
ridiculous
seriousness
studiousness
suspiciously
tremendously
unconsciously
various
vigorously

The following words appear in the reading selection. All of these words contain suffixes. A **suffix** is a word part that is added to the end of a word or the root of a word.

serious   *previously*   *various*
tremendous   *nervousness*

Each word above contains the suffix *ous*. When a word ends in *ous*, it is usually an adjective. Notice that the words *previously* and *nervousness* each contain an additional suffix. The suffix *ly* changes *previous* into an adverb. The suffix *ness* changes *nervous* into a noun.

Rule: **Most adjectives ending in *ous* can be changed to adverbs by adding the suffix *ly*. They can be changed to nouns by adding the suffix *ness*.**

Examples:	*Adjectives*	*Adverbs*	*Nouns*
	serious	seriously	seriousness
	nervous	nervously	nervousness
	tremendous	tremendously	tremendousness

All the words in the Study List contain the suffix *ous*. Focus on this suffix as you learn to spell each word. Notice that the adverbs end with the suffix *ly*. The nouns end with the suffix *ness*. Some of these adverb and noun forms are not commonly used in everyday English. However, it is important to know that you may add a suffix to a word to change its part of speech.

SKILL DRILL 1

Write the following Study List words on the lines provided. Then circle the suffix or suffixes in each word.

1. ridiculous _____

2. miscellaneous _____

3. vigorously _____

4. suspiciously _____

5. courteously _____

6. seriousness _____

7. tremendously _____

8. nervousness _____

9. precious _____

10. various _____

11. studiousness _____

12. enormousness _____

13. unconsciously _____

14. previously _____

15. envious _____

SKILL DRILL 2

The following are short definitions of words from the Study List. Fill the blanks with words from the Study List that match the definitions. If you need help, check the Mini-Dictionary in the back of this book.

1. Many kinds; different _____

2. Devotion to study _____

3. The quality of being serious _____

4. Silly or laughable _____

5. At an earlier time; formerly _____

6. Valuable; much loved _____

7. The state of being restless or uneasy _____

8. Expressing envy; jealous _____

9. Graciously or politely _____

10. Made up of many different parts _____

11. Forcefully or energetically _____

12. In a suspicious way _____

13. Not consciously _____

14. Hugeness _____

15. Enormously _____

SKILL DRILL 3

Fill the blanks in each of the following words to form words from the Study List. Then write the word you have formed on the line provided.

1. court _ _ usly _____

2. vigor _ _ sly _____

3. env _ _ us _____

4. misce _ _ an _ _ us _____

5. prev _ _ usly _____

6. ser _ _ usness _____

7. tremend _ _ sly _____

8. enorm _ _ sness _____

9. uncon _ _ io _ _ ly _____

10. ner _ _ usness _____

11. prec _ _ us _____

12. rid _ _ ul _ _ s _____

13. stud _ _ usness _____

14. var _ _ us _____

15. susp _ _ io _ _ ly _____

SKILL DRILL 4

Fill in the chart below by writing each Study List word in its adjective, adverb, or noun form.

Adjective	Adverb	Noun
studious		
	suspiciously	
		tremendousness
vigorous		
	variously	
		unconsciousness
courteous		
	enormously	
		enviousness
nervous		
	preciously	
		previousness
ridiculous		
	seriously	
miscellaneous		

WORD GAME 13

Use the words in the Study List to complete this crossword puzzle.

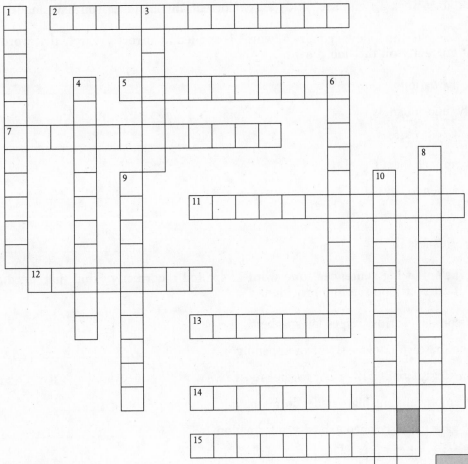

ACROSS

2. Made up of many different parts or things
5. Silly
7. Hugeness
11. Devotion to study
12. Valuable
13. Many kinds; different
14. Enormously
15. Forcefully; energetically

DOWN

1. Graciously or politely
3. Jealous
4. The state of being uneasy
6. The quality of being serious
8. In a suspect manner
9. At an earlier time
10. Not consciously

Study List

courteously
enormousness
envious
miscellaneous
nervousness
precious
previously
ridiculous
seriousness
studiousness
suspiciously
tremendously
unconsciously
various
vigorously

HOW WELL CAN YOU SPELL?

Try to take this practice test without looking back at Lesson 13. After you have finished, check your work against the Study List. Correct any mistakes you have made.

A. One word in each of the following pairs of words is spelled incorrectly. Circle that word and spell it correctly on the line provided.

1. unconschusly, various _____

2. courteously, enormusness _____

3. envious, nerveousness _____

4. preveously, miscellaneous _____

5. ridiculus, tremendously _____

6. suspicusly, vigorously _____

7. precious, seriusness _____

B. In each of the following sentences, one word is spelled incorrectly. Find that word. Then spell it correctly on the line provided.

8. This book contains varius recipes for spaghetti. _____

9. Please shake the carton vigorusly before opening it. _____

10. Donna courteusly opened the door for her mother. _____

11. I am quite envius of your high grades in math. _____

12. The crowd gave us miscelaneous bits of information. _____

13. Mrs. Pierce appreciated the gift tremendusly. _____

14. This is a very preshus piece of antique pottery. _____

15. Barbara is known for her studiusness. _____

CHALLENGE WORDS

Use what you have learned in this lesson to help you remember how to spell the Challenge Words below.

marvelously	prosperous	deliciousness
hazardous	vicious	curiously
melodious	anxiously	strenuous

The Hero

"It is no accident that he plays a lot of heroes," says Carrie Fisher, the princess of *Star Wars* fame. "I think that there are a lot of similarities between the character and the person." She is, of course, speaking of Harrison Ford, today's popular movie hero. Harrison Ford has starred in some of the biggest box-office hits of all time. They include *Star Wars, Return of the Jedi, The Empire Strikes Back, Raiders of the Lost Ark, Indiana Jones and the Temple of Doom,* and *Indiana Jones and the Last Crusade.*

As a boy, Harrison was very shy. He wasn't interested in sports or team play. He admits that he had "a remarkable fear of facing people." It wasn't until much later, in college, that he found an outlet for his shyness—acting. Harrison threw himself wholeheartedly into college dramatics. "It was my first experience working with a group of people on a clearly defined goal," he says. Obviously, he enjoyed himself, because he's been acting ever since.

Eventually, Harrison made his way to Hollywood, where he landed small parts in movies and plays. But something was wrong. He didn't feel that he was doing the kind of acting he had set out to do. He decided that it would be sensible to drop out of acting for a while and learn a trade. So he borrowed a few books from the public library and taught himself woodworking. After a considerable amount of practice, he began to make a living at carpentry. He worked as a carpenter for seven years. With a steady income, he could finally support his wife and two sons.

Harrison learned quite a bit more than carpentry, however. He learned how to work. He became accustomed to starting early in the morning. Often he didn't stop until the job was finished. He began to experience the joy of working hard and doing a good job. Eventually, this dedication overlapped into his acting. "Now I find it difficult to enjoy myself when I'm not working!" he says. That's probably the reason woodworking is still his favorite hobby.

How does Harrison Ford explain his incredible success? "When I began acting, I wasn't confident about myself," he says, "But now I have enough confidence to feel I'm capable of doing the job. It took a long time and a lot of experience."

REVIEWING YOUR READING

Circle the letter beside the word or phrase that best completes the sentence.

1. Harrison Ford's movies are

   a. aimed at teenagers only.
   b. without any special effects.
   c. about life in outer space.
   d. some of the biggest box-office hits of all time.

2. As a boy, Harrison was

   a. outgoing and popular.
   b. athletic.
   c. shy.
   d. interested in dramatics.

3. Harrison's interest in acting began in

   a. grammar school.
   b. junior high school.
   c. high school.
   d. college.

4. Harrison's college acting experience was the first time he ever

   a. worked with a group of people on a clearly defined goal.
   b. played a hero.
   c. enjoyed himself.
   d. played a detective.

5. When Harrison first arrived in Hollywood, he

   a. directed small groups of actors.
   b. worked as a carpenter.
   c. got small parts in movies and plays.
   d. immediately quit acting.

6. Harrison's dedication to work overlapped into his acting. The word *dedication* means

   a. poor attitude.
   b. need for money.
   c. commitment.
   d. lack of commitment.

7. You can conclude that Harrison dropped out of acting because

   a. he wasn't doing the kind of acting he thought he should be doing.
   b. no one would give him a job.
   c. the parts he played were all heroes.
   d. he liked carpentry better.

8. You can conclude that today Harrison

   a. dislikes what he is doing.
   b. would prefer to be a carpenter.
   c. enjoys his work very much.
   d. has no hobbies.

FIGURING THE FACTS

Decide whether the following statements are true or false. Write *T* on the line if the statement is true. If the statement is false, change the statement to make it true. Cross out the incorrect word or phrase in the sentence. Then, if necessary, write the correct word or phrase on the line.

1. Carrie Fisher thinks Harrison Ford is like a real hero.   _____

2. As a boy, Harrison had a fear of animals.   _____

3. He learned woodworking from another actor.   _____

4. Eventually, Harrison earned a living at carpentry.   _____

5. Harrison has two sons.   _____

6. As a carpenter, he began work late in the day.   _____

7. Often he kept working until the job was done.   _____

8. When he began acting, Harrison had very little confidence.   _____

9. His favorite hobby is going to the movies.   _____

10. Harrison finds it hard to enjoy himself when he isn't working.   _____

WHAT'S YOUR OPINION?

1. What do you think Harrison Ford means by the "joy" of working?

_____

_____

_____

_____

_____

2. Self-confidence has played a large part in Harrison Ford's success. Why is self-confidence so important?

_____

_____

_____

_____

_____

DEVELOPING SPELLING SKILLS

Study List

comparable
compatible
considerable
dependable
eligible
incredible
indelible
irresistable
irresponsible
legible
noticeable
reliable
remarkable
sensible
valuable

The following words appear in the reading selection.

remarkable   incredible
considerable   sensible

As you say these words, you will notice that the **suffixes** *able* and *ible* sound quite similar. Words with these endings are often confused. Here is a hint that may be used as a general guide: If the base is a full word, then the ending is probably *able*.

Examples: **remark** + **able** = *remarkable*
consider + **able** = *considerable*

incred + **ible** = *incredible*
sens + **ible** = *sensible*

However, there are many exceptions. Can you tell which Study List words are exceptions? Since there is no absolute rule for spelling these words, they must be memorized.

SKILL DRILL 1

Write the following Study List words on the lines provided. Then circle the *able* or *ible* suffix in each word.

1. irresistible _____
2. incredible _____
3. eligible _____
4. compatible _____
5. valuable _____
6. remarkable _____
7. noticeable _____

8. indelible _____
9. dependable _____
10. comparable _____
11. considerable _____
12. sensible _____
13. reliable _____
14. legible _____

15. irresponsible _____

SKILL DRILL 2

The following are short definitions of words from the Study List. Fill the blanks with words from the Study List that match the definitions. If you need help, check the Mini-Dictionary in the back of this book.

1. Having great worth _____
2. Able to be relied on _____
3. Able to be depended on _____
4. Not erasable; permanent _____
5. Worthy of comparison _____
6. Difficult to believe; astonishing _____
7. Not able to be resisted _____
8. Able to be read _____
9. Not responsible _____
10. Worth consideration; much or large _____
11. Able to get along together _____
12. Fit to be chosen; qualified _____
13. Easily seen or noticed _____
14. Having good judgment or sense _____
15. Worthy of comment _____

SKILL DRILL 3

Fill the blanks in each of the following words to form words from the Study List.
Then write the words you have formed on the lines provided.

1. val _ _ ble _____

2. remar _ _ ble _____

3. le _ _ ble _____

4. irresis _ _ ble _____

5. incre _ _ ble _____

6. eli _ _ ble _____

7. compat _ ble _____

8. sen _ _ ble _____

9. notic _ _ ble _____

10. irrespon _ _ ble _____

11. inde _ _ ble _____

12. depen _ _ ble _____

13. compa _ _ ble _____

14. conside _ _ ble _____

15. rel _ _ ble _____

SKILL DRILL 4

Answer the following questions by using words from the Study List.

Which words begin with the prefix *ir*?

1. _____   2. _____

Which words begin with the prefix *in*?

3. _____   4. _____

Which words begin with the prefixes *con* or *com*?

5. _____   6. _____   7. _____

Which words begin with the prefix *re*?

8. _____   9. _____

Which word begins with the prefix *de*?

10. _____

Which words end with *gible*?

11. _____   12. _____

Which word contains the root word *value*?

13. _____

Which word contains the root word *sense*?

14. _____

Which word contains the word *notice*?

15. _____

WORD GAME 14

The words from the Study List are used in this puzzle. The numbers of the clues match the numbers in the puzzle. Read the clues below. Then write your answers in the puzzle blocks.

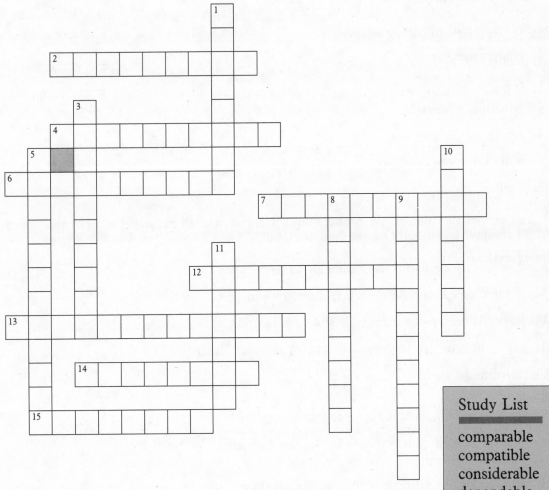

Study List

comparable
compatible
considerable
dependable
eligible
incredible
indelible
irresistible
irresponsible
legible
noticeable
reliable
remarkable
sensible
valuable

ACROSS

2. Permanently marked
4. Easily seen
6. Able to get along together
7. Astonishing
12. Able to be depended on
13. Not responsible
14. Levelheaded
15. Fit to be chosen

DOWN

1. Able to be relied on
3. Worthy of comparison
5. Worth consideration
8. Worthy of comment
9. Not able to be resisted
10. Of great value
11. Able to be read

HOW WELL CAN YOU SPELL?

Try to take this practice test without looking back at Lesson 14. After you have finished, check your work against the Study List. Correct any mistakes you have made.

A. One word in each of the following pairs of words is spelled incorrectly. Circle that word and spell it correctly on the line provided.

1. considerible, compatible   _____

2. comparable, dependible   _____

3. eligible, incredable   _____

4. indelible, irresistable   _____

5. irresponsible, relyable   _____

6. remarkible, valuable   _____

7. legible, sensable   _____

B. In each of the following sentences, one word is spelled incorrectly. Find that word. Then spell it correctly on the line provided.

8. The jewelry we found was extremely valueable.   _____

9. If there was a stain on the shirt, it wasn't noticable.   _____

10. Ramon's note was written in legable handwriting.   _____

11. Janet thought that leaving was an irresponsable thing to do.   _____

12. Please sign your name in indelable ink.   _____

13. Each of our students is eligeable for the scholarship. _____

14. These coins are comparible to those used in ancient times.   _____

15. Your computer software is compatable with my computer. _____

CHALLENGE WORDS

Use what you have learned in this lesson to help you remember how to spell the Challenge Words below.

digestible	accessible	detectable
divisible	incomprehensible	permissible
inflammable	sociable	sizable

Save Our Smiles

Can you imagine not being able to bite into a delicious apple or a golden ear of corn? Many people cannot eat such foods because their teeth are in such bad shape. The fact is that over 30 million people in North America are in grave danger of losing their teeth. The problem is periodontal disease. It usually affects three out of every four people.

Like cavities, periodontal disease is caused by germs called *bacteria*. These bacteria can destroy the bones that support each tooth. Is there a way to destroy the bacteria before they destroy your teeth? The answer is yes! Basically, the secret is to clean away the bacteria. These tiny demons hide in the crevices between your teeth. They live on food and other substances in your mouth. This produces *plaque* (pronounced *plak*)—a gummy film, or coating, that covers your teeth. Later, the plaque hardens and forms a hard substance called *tartar*. If the tartar is not scraped away, it can build up and cause the gums to swell. The roots of the teeth become weak, and eventually, the teeth fall out.

Logically enough, the solution for keeping your teeth healthy and free from bacteria is simple. Daily brushing, proper use of dental floss, and regular visits to the dentist are most important. Everyone knows how to brush his or her teeth, and good dentists are easy to find. But many people don't know about dental floss. It is a special kind of string that is used to clean out the bacteria between the teeth. One high school student asked his dentist if it was really necessary to floss all his teeth. "Not necessarily," the dentist replied. "Only the ones you want to keep!"

All of this may seem like a lot of effort. But the results are worth it. As one dentist said, "Be true to your teeth, or they'll be false to you."

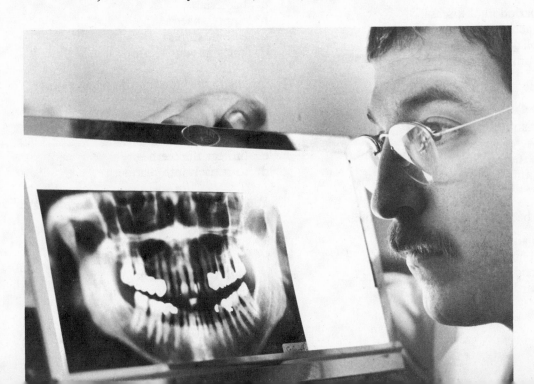

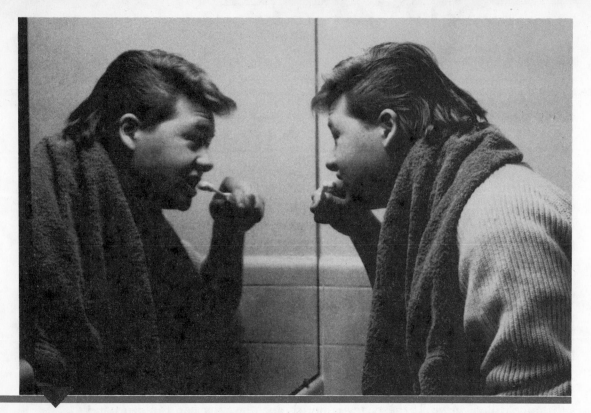

REVIEWING YOUR READING

Circle the letter beside the word or phrase that best completes the sentence.

1. In North America, the number of people in danger of losing their teeth is
   a. less than 1,000.
   b. more than 30 million.
   c. less than 30 million.
   d. more than 20 billion.

2. A major concern in dental care is a problem called
   a. periodontal disease.
   b. bacteria illness.
   c. plaque disease.
   d. gummy film disease.

3. Periodontal disease begins with
   a. plaque.
   b. bacteria.
   c. tartar.
   d. gummy film.

4. The bacteria in the mouth produce
   a. plaque.
   b. dental floss.
   c. food.
   d. hard teeth.

5. When plaque hardens, it is called
   a. bacteria.
   b. cavities.
   c. tooth decay.
   d. tartar.

6. "These tiny demons hide in the crevices between your teeth." The word *crevices* means
   a. bacteria.
   b. empty spaces.
   c. evil creatures.
   d. holes in your teeth.

7. You can conclude that if tartar is never scraped away, it can
   a. cause teeth to fall out.
   b. strengthen the gums.
   c. protect the teeth.
   d. turn back into plaque.

8. You can conclude that the use of dental floss is
   a. not necessary for dental care.
   b. good to use but not necessary.
   c. better than brushing.
   d. necessary for good dental care.

FIGURING THE FACTS

Decide whether the following statements are true or false. Write *T* on the line if the statement is true. If the statement is false, change the statement to make it true. Cross out the incorrect word or phrase in the sentence. Then, if necessary, write the correct word or phrase on the line.

1. Periodontal disease affects three out of every four people.   _____

2. Periodontal disease is caused by cavities.   _____

3. It can destroy the bones that support the teeth.   _____

4. Bacteria live on substances in the mouth.   _____

5. Plaque is a gummy film that covers the teeth.   _____

6. Plaque eventually becomes soft.   _____

7. Soft plaque is called *tartar*.   _____

8. Tartar can build up and cause the teeth to swell.   _____

9. Dental floss is used to clean out bacteria.   _____

10. Good dental care includes brushing and flossing.   _____

WHAT'S YOUR OPINION?

1. If periodontal disease can be prevented, why do you think so many people are in danger of losing their teeth?

_____

_____

_____

_____

_____

2. Why do you think good dental care is important?

_____

_____

_____

_____

_____

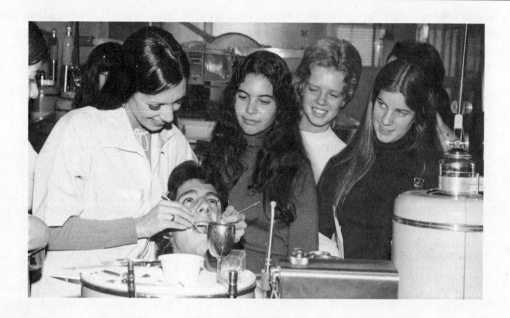

DEVELOPING SPELLING SKILLS

Study List

annually
artificially
artistically
athletically
basically
eventually
generally
historically
logically
mathematically
musically
physically
politically
typically
usually

A **noun** is the name of a person, place or thing.

An **adjective** is a word that describes a noun.

An **adverb** is a word that describes an action.

Look at the following sentence.

The *beautiful leaves* will fall *eventually.*

The word *leaves* is a **noun**. *Beautiful* is an **adjective** because it describes the noun *leaves. Eventually* is an **adverb** because it describes the action *will fall.*

Sometimes nouns and adjectives can be changed to adverbs.

Rule: **To change most nouns or adjectives to adverbs, add *ly*, even when the word already ends with *l*. However, when a word ends in *c*, add *ally*.**

Examples:	*Adjectives*	*Adverbs*
	eventual	eventually
	usual	usually
	basic	basically
	Nouns	*Adverbs*
	logic	logically
	music	musically

Notice that all the words in the Study List are adverbs.

SKILL DRILL 1

Change the following nouns or adjectives to adverbs by adding *ly* **or** *ally*. **Write your answers on the lines provided.**

1. usual _____
2. annual _____
3. typical _____
4. physical _____
5. artistic _____
6. general _____
7. mathematic _____

8. logic _____
9. athletic _____
10. political _____
11. music _____
12. eventual _____
13. historic _____
14. basic _____

15. artificial _____

SKILL DRILL 2

The following are short definitions of words from the Study List. Fill the blanks with words from the Study List that match the definitions. If you need help, check the Mini-Dictionary in the back of this book.

1. In a basic way _____
2. Yearly; every year _____
3. In a usual way _____
4. In a typical manner _____
5. In a political manner _____
6. In a physical or bodily manner _____
7. In an athletic manner _____
8. Not naturally; not in a genuine way _____
9. In an artistic way _____
10. In the end; finally _____
11. In most cases _____
12. In a logical manner; reasonably _____
13. In a musical way _____
14. According to mathematics _____
15. According to history _____

SKILL DRILL 3

Write the noun *or* the adjective form of each adverb below.

1. musically _____
2. logically _____
3. artistically _____
4. usually _____
5. politically _____
6. generally _____
7. basically _____

8. mathematically _____
9. annually _____
10. historically _____
11. typically _____
12. physically _____
13. eventually _____
14. athletically _____

15. artificially _____

SKILL DRILL 4

Fill in each blank with the adverb form of the adjective or noun in parentheses to form a Study List word.

1. We (usual) _____ go to the movies on Saturday.
2. We (general) _____ meet in the gym.
3. This biography is (historical) _____ accurate.
4. The inspector (logic) _____ solved the case.
5. Solve the problem (mathematical) _____.
6. The birds sang (music) _____.
7. Those flowers bloom (annual) _____.
8. The gymnasts leaped (athlete) _____.
9. Janet is (basic) _____ a very shy person.
10. We will (eventual) _____ see the film.
11. Acrobatics is (physical) _____ quite strenuous.
12. Jeff is very active (political) _____.
13. This material is made (artificial) _____.
14. The weather is (typical) _____ warm this spring.
15. The flowers were arranged (artistic) _____.

Study List

annually
artificially
artistically
athletically
basically
eventually
generally
historically
logically
mathematically
musically
physically
politically
typically
usually

WORD GAME 15

The words from the Study List are scrambled on the left. Unscramble each word and write it correctly in the spaces on the right. If you unscramble the words correctly, you will find the answer to the puzzle question by reading the shaded column downward. Write your answer on the line below.

CITAMEHTAMALLY

TISTCIARALLY

SUUALLY

CISABALLY

RAENEGLLY

O
F

HLETICATALLY

GICOLALLY

CITILPOALLY

YPTCIALLY

TORICHISALLY

SICPHYALLY

UNNAALLY

CISUMALLY

FICIARTIALLY

VENTEUALLY

What is it that helps keep your teeth together? _____

HOW WELL CAN YOU SPELL?

Try to take this practice test without looking back at Lesson 15. After you have finished, check your work against the Study List. Correct any mistakes you have made.

A. One word in each of the following pairs of words is spelled incorrectly. Circle that word and spell it correctly on the line provided.

1. athleticaly, eventually   _____

2. usually, artisticaly   _____

3. generaly, artificially   _____

4. basically, logicaly   _____

5. musicaly, historically   _____

6. physicaly, mathematically   _____

7. typically, politicaly   _____

8. annualy, artificially   _____

B. In each of the following sentences, one word is spelled incorrectly. Find that word. Then spell it correctly on the line provided.

9. We usualy get up early on Sunday mornings.   _____

10. Dancers typicaly practice several hours a day.   _____

11. The solution can be figured out mathematicaly.   _____

12. These plants will grow eventualy.   _____

13. Some gases are artificialy produced in the laboratory.   _____

14. There are basicaly three parts to each question. _____

15. Historicaly, these documents are quite authentic. _____

CHALLENGE WORDS

Use what you have learned in this lesson to help you remember how to spell the Challenge Words below.

initially	emotionally	additionally
nationally	intentionally	incidentally
patriotically	critically	apologetically

Champion of Children

"I can be tough as nails, just as anybody who believes in anything has to be tough," claims Marian Wright Edelman. She has been labeled a woman of vision and intelligence, and she is the most powerful champion of children's rights in the country today.

Seeing the need to protect America's future through its youth, Marian founded the Children's Defense Fund. It is a group that represents the interests of the 63 million children who make up the youth population.

What does the Children's Defense Fund do? It represents the needs of the nation's children. The organization campaigns for children in areas ranging from poverty and health care to education and child abuse. "I think what the Children's Defense Fund is about," Marian explains, "is trying to influence politicans to do what is right for the nation, and what is right for the nation's weakest citizens."

Marian never hesitates to talk about the importance of caring for the youth of America. "Our children are either going to be invested in now and they're going to grow up and produce for us, or they're going to grow up and shoot at us because we have not taken care of them."

Most of her experiences revolved around the Baptist Church where her father was the minister. Marian explains, "He made it very clear to me that I could be anything, do anything. He told me how important it was not to let anything get between me and my education, and everything I could be."

Edelman attended Spelman College in Atlanta. She became angered by the plight of black and poor people in America and decided to do something about it. She decided to go back to school and get her law degree. After graduating from Yale Law School, she became the first black woman to practice law in the State of Mississippi.

"There was never a time when I was growing up that I didn't think I could change the world. I don't think enough young people today feel they can change the world." When asked if she has changed the world, Marian says, "I hope I've made a difference. But I haven't changed it as much as I still want to change it."

REVIEWING YOUR READING

Circle the letter beside the word or phrase that best completes the sentence.

1. Marian Wright Edelman campaigns for

   a. women's rights.
   b. children's rights.
   c. political freedom.
   d. children's votes.

2. Marian is a graduate of

   a. Atlanta University.
   b. University of Mississippi.
   c. Spelman College.
   d. Yale Law School.

3. You can conclude that Marian feels children are the "weakest citizens" because

   a. they have needs that are not met.
   b. they do not have the right to vote.
   c. they cannot read.
   d. they are physically not strong.

4. Marian decided to get her law degree after she

   a. had seen the plight of poor people in America.
   b. had heard of the need for good lawyers.
   c. had seen the plight of poor people in Russia.
   d. had heard there were no woman lawyers in Mississippi.

5. Ms. Edelman is

   a. the founder of The Children's Defense Fund.
   b. a senator from Mississippi.
   c. the founder of a Baptist Church.
   d. a teacher at Yale University.

6. America's youth population is composed of

   a. 63 million children.
   b. 6 million children.
   c. 36 million children.
   d. 3 million children.

7. From the story you can conclude that as a child, Marian felt

   a. trapped by her surroundings.
   b. she could do anything she set her mind to do.
   c. she should fight for herself and other children.
   d. children had a great deal of power.

8. From the story, you can conclude that Marian Wright Edelman

   a. has completed her work for children.
   b. intends to continue fighting for children's rights.
   c. is now working for women's rights.
   d. will be running for state senator.

FIGURING THE FACTS

Decide whether the following statements are true or false. Write *T* on the line if the statement is true. If the statement is false, change the statement to make it true. Cross out the incorrect word or phrase in the sentence. Then, if necessary, write the correct word or phrase on the line.

1. Marian's father was a state senator.   _____

2. The Children's Defense Fund fights for children's rights.   _____

3. Marian believed she could be anything and do anything.   _____

4. Marian thinks she's changed the world enough.   _____

5. Marian is a graduate of Yale Law School.   _____

6. Most of Marian's childhood centered around work.   _____

7. Marian's father told her how important education was.   _____

8. Marian is the second black woman to practice Law in Mississippi.   _____

9. The Children's Defense Fund works with legislators.   _____

10. Marian attended Spelman College in Atlanta.   _____

WHAT'S YOUR OPINION?

1. When Marion was growing up she felt that "she could change the world." Do you feel that you can "change the world"? Why or why not?

_____

_____

_____

_____

2. Do you agree with Marion when she says "Our children are either going to be invested in now or when they grow up they're going to shoot at us because we have not taken care of them"? Why or why not?

_____

_____

_____

_____

DEVELOPING SPELLING SKILLS

Study List

characterize
circumference
compromise
endurance
importance
improvise
influence
intelligence
interference
lengthwise
merchandise
modernize
organize
resemblance
sterilize

Remember: **A** *suffix* **is a word part that is added to the end of a word or a root.**

Some ·suffixes sound similar, although they may be spelled differently. Two of the following words appear in the reading selection. Each word ends with a suffix.

importance   intelligence   modernize

As you say these words, notice how similar the suffixes *ance* and *ence* sound. The *ise* and *ize* suffixes also sound alike. Therefore, it is especially important to note the spelling differences in these words. Since there is no absolute rule for spelling these words, they must be memorized.

As you learn the words on the Study List, pay extra attention to the suffixes.

SKILL DRILL 1

Write the following Study List words on the lines provided. Then circle the *ise, ize, ance,* or *ence* ending in each word.

1. sterilize _____
2. characterize _____
3. organize _____
4. compromise _____
5. importance _____
6. merchandise _____
7. interference _____

8. resemblance _____
9. circumference _____
10. modernize _____
11. endurance _____
12. improvise _____
13. lengthwise _____
14. intelligence _____

15. influence _____

SKILL DRILL 2

The following are short definitions of words from the Study List. Fill the blanks with words from the Study List that match the definitions. If you need help, check the Mini-Dictionary in the back of this book.

1. The boundary line of a circle _____
2. The settlement of a dispute by both sides giving in _____
3. To make free of germs _____
4. To arrange in order _____
5. To bring up to date or make modern _____
6. Goods for sale _____
7. In the direction of the length _____
8. Likeness; similar in appearance _____
9. To describe characteristics _____
10. Power to affect another person _____
11. The ability to learn _____
12. Significance; the state of being important _____
13. The ability to last or keep going _____
14. To make something up without preparation _____
15. The act of interfering or interrupting _____

SKILL DRILL 3

Fill the blanks in each of the following words to form words from the Study List. Then write the words you have formed on the lines provided.

1. influ _ _ ce _____

2. interfer _ _ ce _____

3. merchand _ _ e _____

4. organi _ _ _____

5. circumfer _ _ ce _____

6. endur _ _ ce _____

7. sterili _ _ _____

8. intellig _ _ ce _____

9. lengthw _ _ e _____

10. moderni _ _ _____

11. character _ _ e _____

12. compromi _ _ _____

13. import _ _ ce _____

14. resembl _ _ ce _____

15. improvi _ _ _____

SKILL DRILL 4

Answer the following questions by using words from the Study List.

Which words end with the suffix *ance*?

1. _____   2. _____

3. _____

Which words end with the suffix *ence*?

4. _____   5. _____

6. _____   7. _____

Which words end with the suffix *ize*?

8. _____   9. _____

10. _____   11. _____

Which words end with the suffix *ise*?

12. _____   13. _____

14. _____   15. _____

WORD GAME 16

The words from the Study List are used in this puzzle. The numbers of the clues match the numbers in the puzzle. Read the clues below. Then write your answers in the puzzle blocks.

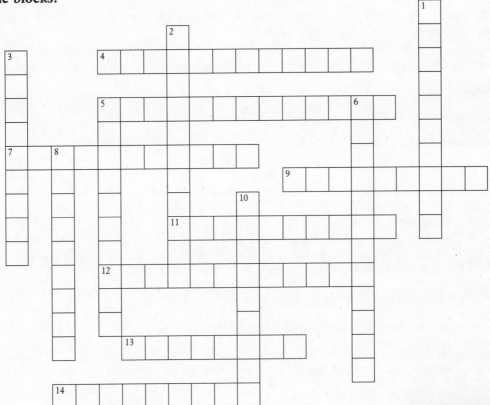

ACROSS

4. Smartness
5. The boundary line of a circle
7. Similar in looks
9. To make up without preparation
11. Significance
12. The act of interfering
13. To arrange
14. Power to affect

DOWN

1. In the direction of the length
2. Goods for sale
3. The ability to last
5. A way of settling an argument
6. To describe someone
8. To make free of germs
10. To bring up to date

Study List

characterize
circumference
compromise
endurance
importance
improvise
influence
intelligence
interference
lengthwise
merchandise
modernize
organize
resemblance
sterilize

HOW WELL CAN YOU SPELL?

Try to take this practice test without looking back at Lesson 16. After you have finished, check your work against the Study List. Correct any mistakes you have made.

A. One word in each of the following pairs of words is spelled incorrectly. Circle that word and spell it correctly on the line provided.

1. intelligance, improvise   _____

2. circumference, characterise   _____

3. endurance, resemblence   _____

4. modernise, merchandise   _____

5. interferance, influence   _____

6. importence, compromise   _____

7. sterilize, organise   _____

B. In each of the following sentences, one word is spelled incorrectly. Find that word. Then spell it correctly on the line provided.

8. Please measure the trunk lengthwize.   _____

9. The nurse will sterilise the instruments for the operation.   _____

10. There was not much merchandize left on the store's shelves.   _____

11. After talking, we finally reached a compromize.   _____

12. Joanne has broken the record in the endurence test.   _____

13. The circumferance of the barrel was greater than we thought.   _____

14. Louise will probably have to improvize her speech.   _____

15. The influance of Juan's father helped him succeed.   _____

CHALLENGE WORDS

Use what you have learned in this lesson to help you remember how to spell the Challenge Words below.

colonize	civilize	fertilize
clockwise	televise	conference
resistance	inheritance	patience

Husky Victory

It was the last day of the race. Libby Riddles and her thirteen huskies had already traveled over one thousand miles. A violent blizzard was raging. The blinding snow was so dense that the race markers were invisible. Only one hundred thirty miles were left to reach the finish line. All the other competitors decided to wait out the storm, but not Libby. "I'm going to try it," she thought, "even if it's crazy." Her daring decision won her the race. That made Libby Riddles the first woman ever to win the Iditarod Trail Dog Sled Race.

It took seventeen days for Libby to complete the total distance—eleven hundred thirty-five miles. The Iditarod Trail stretches from Anchorage, Alaska, to Nome, Alaska. It cuts through two mountain ranges and across the Yukon River. Libby's victory is a tribute to her persistence and adventuresome spirit. But let's not forget her four-legged crew!

In long-distance races, up to twenty-two dogs can be used to pull a sled. Each animal's position in the team depends on physical and mental ability. The most alert and intelligent animal is placed at the head of the pack. This is the *lead dog*. The lead dog must be able to respond to the commands of the driver and set the pace for the other animals. Second in the lineup is the *point dog*. This animal acts as a backup for the lead dog in case there is any problem. Next are the *team dogs* in the middle of the pack. They are usually the strongest because they do the most pulling. Last in the lineup are the *wheel dogs*. They are directly in front of the sled.

Some people believe that dog sled racing is cruel to the animals. Other people claim that these dogs "were born to run." They point to the excitement among the dogs on race day. There is more barking and howling than at feeding time in the kennel. The dogs seem anxious to get out and begin.

Libby knows she couldn't have won without the help of her animals. "They are a fine bunch of dogs," she said. "I did my part to keep them happy and healthy." What did Libby do with the $50,000 prize? She took a trip to Hawaii, and bought a box of biscuits for each of the dogs!

REVIEWING YOUR READING

Circle the letter beside the word or phrase that best completes the sentence.

1. Libby Riddles is the first woman to

   a. travel by dog sled.
   b. cross the Yukon River.
   c. win the Iditarod Trail Dog Sled
      Race.
   d. win the Nome Dog Sled Race.

2. Libby was the only competitor to

   a. continue on during the windstorm.
   b. wait out the blizzard.
   c. continue on during the blizzard.
   d. reach the finish line.

3. The Iditarod Trail stretches from

   a. Juneau to Nome, Alaska.
   b. Anchorage to Nome, Alaska.
   c. the Rocky Mountains to Alaska.
   d. the Yukon River to Juneau, Alaska.

4. The total distance Libby covered was

   a. twenty-two miles.
   b. eleven hundred thirty-five miles.
   c. one hundred thirty miles.
   d. one thousand miles.

5. The blinding snow was so dense that
   the race markers were invisible. The
   word *dense* means

   a. thin.
   b. clear.
   c. thick.
   d. cold.

6. Libby's victory is a tribute to her
   persistence and adventuresome spirit.
   The word *persistence* means

   a. hesitation.
   b. laziness.
   c. physical strength.
   d. determination.

7. According to the selection, you can
   conclude that the lead dog must be

   a. intelligent and alert.
   b. the strongest of the pack.
   c. able to point.
   d. able to do the most pulling.

8. You can conclude that Libby probably
   would not have won the race if she had

   a. a larger sled.
   b. not taken a chance.
   c. a more intelligent lead dog.
   d. a larger team.

FIGURING THE FACTS

Decide whether the following statements are true or false. Write *T* on the line if the statement is true. If the statement is false, change the statement to make it true. Cross out the incorrect word or phrase in the sentence. Then, if necessary, write the correct word or phrase on the line.

1. By the last day of the race, Libby had one thousand miles left to reach the finish line.   _____

2. The blizzard made the race markers more visible.   _____

3. Libby knew that going on in the blizzard might be foolish.   _____

4. It took seventy days to complete the trip.   _____

5. The Iditarod Trail crosses the Yukon River.   _____

6. On a dog sled team, there can be as many as thirty animals.   _____

7. The point dog acts as a backup for the lead dog.   _____

8. The wheel dogs are directly in front of the sled.   _____

9. The team dogs set the pace for the other animals.   _____

10. The team dogs are usually the strongest of the pack.   _____

WHAT'S YOUR OPINION?

1. Libby had to take a chance in order to win. How important do you think it is to take chances in life?

_____

_____

_____

_____

2. Some people believe that dog sled racing is cruel to the animals. Other people claim that these dogs "were born to run." What do you think?

_____

_____

_____

_____

DEVELOPING SPELLING SKILLS

Study List

division
eight hundred
five-hundredths
fourteen
kilometer
milligram
multiplication
ninety-eight
one-fifth
perpendicular
seven-tenths
six million
subtraction
three-fourths
two-thousandths

The following words appear in the reading selection.

one hundred thirty   twenty-two   thirteen   one thousand

It is important to know how to spell numbers because you are often asked to write them out. Numbers can be tricky because many require the use of a hyphen. The rules below will help you remember when to write numbers with hyphens.

Rule: **Use a hyphen when writing the compound numbers from twenty-one to ninety-nine.**

Example: ninety-eight

Rule: **Use a hyphen when writing the numerator and denominator in fractions.**

Example: one-fifth

Rule: **Use a hyphen when writing a decimal.**

Example: two-thousandths

The Study List contains numbers and words that you will use in math and science. Study these words carefully. They will serve as models for other numbers and similar words.

SKILL DRILL 1

Write the following Study List words on the lines provided.

1. two-thousandths _____

2. subtraction _____

3. seven-tenths _____

4. one-fifth _____

5. multiplication _____

6. kilometer _____

7. division _____

8. three-fourths _____

9. six million _____

10. perpendicular _____

11. ninety-eight _____

12. milligram _____

13. fourteen _____

14. five-hundredths _____

15. eight hundred _____

SKILL DRILL 2

A. Spell out the words for the following numbers on the lines provided.

1. 1/5 _____

2. 7/10 _____

3. 800 _____

4. .002 _____

5. 3/4 _____

6. .05 _____

7. 14 _____

8. 98 _____

9. 6,000,000 _____

B. Fill the blanks with words from the Study List that match the following definitions. If you need help, check the Mini-Dictionary in the back of this book.

10. The process of dividing one number into another _____

11. The process of multiplying one number by another _____

12. The process of subtracting one number from another _____

13. One thousand meters _____

14. One-thousandth of a gram _____

15. A line at right angles to another line _____

SKILL DRILL 3

Fill the blanks in each of the following words to form words from the Study List. Then write the word you have formed on the line provided.

1. f _ _ rteen _____

2. mi _ _ igram _____

3. ni _ _ ty-eight _____

4. p _ _ pen _ _ cular _____

5. six mi _ _ _ on _____

6. _ _ ght hundred _____

7. subtr _ _ tion _____

8. kilom _ _ _ r _____

9. multi _ _ _ cation _____

10. one-fi _ _ _ _____

11. sev _ _ -tenths _____

12. div _ _ _ on _____

13. five-hundre _ _ _ s _____

14. three-f _ _ _ ths _____

15. two-thous _ _ _ ths _____

SKILL DRILL 4

Answer the following questions by using words from the Study List.

Which words are numbers that are not written with a hyphen?

1. _____   2. _____

3. _____

Which words are written in the form of decimals or fractions?

4. _____   5. _____

6. _____   7. _____

8. _____

Which words describe mathematical procedures?

9. _____   10. _____

11. _____

Which words describe units of measurement?

12. _____   13. _____

Which word describes a line at right angles?

14. _____

Which word is a compound number that is written with a hyphen?

15. _____

Study List
division
eight hundred
five-hundredths
fourteen
kilometer
milligram
multiplication
ninety-eight
one-fifth
perpendicular
seven-tenths
six million
subtraction
three-fourths
two-thousandths

WORD GAME 17

On the left are hints for the puzzle spaces on the right. If you fill in the spaces with the correct Study List word, you will find the answer to the puzzle question by reading the shaded column downward. Write your answer on the line below.

6,000,000

1/5

process of subtracting

801 − 1 =

7/10

one-thousandth of a gram

process of dividing

3/4

sixteen minus two equals

.05

ninety-six plus two equals

process of multiplying

.002

a line at right angles

1,000 meters

What do you call the smartest animal on a dog sled team?

The _____

HOW WELL CAN YOU SPELL?

Try to take this practice test without looking back at **Lesson 17**. After you have finished, check your work against the Study List. Correct any mistakes you have made.

A. One word in each of the following pairs of words is spelled incorrectly. Circle that word and spell it correctly on the line provided.

1. devision, kilometer   _____

2. eight hunred, multiplication   _____

3. ninety-eight, five-hundreths   _____

4. forteen, one-fifth   _____

5. perpendicular, miligram   _____

6. six million, sevin-tenths   _____

7. two-thousands, three-fourths   _____

B. In each of the following sentences, one word is spelled incorrectly. Find that word. Then spell it correctly on the line provided.

8. Multipication is simple if you learn the tables.   _____

9. Greg got ninty-eight percent of the questions right.   _____

10. Third Street is purpendicular to Jasmine Road.   _____

11. Over six milion people will see this telecast.   _____

12. With one kilomiter left, Joan took the lead in the race.   _____

13. Jennifer was having trouble learning subtrakshun.   _____

14. Three-forths of the pie has already been eaten.   _____

15. Our survey covered one-fifthe of the neighborhood.   _____

CHALLENGE WORDS

The Challenge Words below are often used in math and science.

parallel	quadrilateral	polygon
decimeter	centimeter	trapezoid
milliliter	microscope	thermometer

Big Bird

The scene is a dry lake bed, in the desert 70 miles outside of Los Angeles. A camera crew and a group of scientists have gathered. They have come to witness the flight of a dinosaur. Impossible! Dinosaurs disappeared from the Earth over 63 million years ago.

Of course, the bird is not a real dinosaur, but a recreation. It is the work of a team of biologists, engineers, inventors, aerodynamicists, and paleontologists. (Aerodynamicists are scientists who study flight. Paleontologists are scientists who study fossils.) They have put together a working model of what they think is the largest living creature ever to fly. The huge reptile is a member of the pterosaur family.

The project began over 20 years ago in Texas. A paleontologist there had discovered some fossil remains. As he began to piece the bones together, he realized the bones were part of a giant reptile's wing. The wingspan was unusual in its size, 36 feet. That's about as wide as four cars parked side by side. Scientists were doubtful that any animal of such size could have flown at all.

The challenge was on to see if, in fact, the huge pterosaur could have flown. But it was not good enough just to have the giant bird glide across the sky. The scientists wanted the bird to flap its wings and stay aloft, just as its real-life predecessor did millions of years ago.

The huge replica was painstakingly reconstructed from the fossil remains. The model is smaller, however, than the original fossil, about half the size. It is constructed from ultra-light materials. Radio controlled electronics provide the wing movement. When it flaps its wings, it's like a dream from the past.

The experiment is the concept of Paul MacCready, an aeronautical engineer. According to MacCready, "One purpose of the project is to show that what Man is doing with flight today isn't all that different from what Nature has been doing for a hundred million years."

REVIEWING YOUR READING

Circle the letter beside the word or phrase that best completes the sentence.

1. The pterosaur experiment was held

   a. in Los Angeles.
   b. in a lake.
   c. in a dry lake bed.
   d. outside of a desert.

2. Dinosaurs disappeared from the Earth about

   a. 63 million years ago.
   b. 200 million years ago.
   c. 6 million years ago.
   d. 36 million years ago.

3. A paleontologist is a scientist that studies

   a. flight.
   b. birds.
   c. engineering.
   d. fossils.

4. The team of creators of the pterosaur included

   a. physicists and lawyers.
   b. inventors and zoo keepers.
   c. fighter pilots.
   d. biologists and engineers.

5. The model of the pterosaur is about

   a. half the size of the original fossil.
   b. the same size as the original fossil.
   c. twice the size as the original fossil.
   d. one third the size of the original fossil.

6. The replica was painstakingly reconstructed. The word *painstakingly* most probably means

   a. very beautifully.
   b. quite carefully.
   c. haphazardly.
   d. painfully.

7. Scientists built this model

   a. to find out if the pterosaur actually could fly.
   b. as a human powered bird model.
   c. for solar heating.
   d. to find a natural energy source.

8. You can conclude that Paul MacCready wants people to

   a. be more aware of flying animals.
   b. look for fossils.
   c. be more aware of nature.
   d. build model dinosaurs.

FIGURING THE FACTS

Decide whether the following statements are true or false. Write *T* on the line if the statement is true. If the statement is false, change the statement to make it true. Cross out the incorrect word or phrase in the sentence. Then, if necessary, write the correct word or phrase on the line.

1. Paleontologists study fossils. _____

2. Wing movement for the model was radio-controlled. _____

3. The model was made from heavy-duty materials. _____

4. The wingspan of the original fossil was quite small. _____

5. Aerodynamicists study crawling animals. _____

6. The original pterosaur fossils were found in Ohio. _____

7. The pterosaur was probably the smallest of all flying creatures. _____

8. The experiment was the concept of an aeronautical engineer. _____

9. The wingspan of the model was larger than the fossil. _____

10. The pterosaur model had wings that flapped. _____

WHAT'S YOUR OPINION?

1. Do you think demonstrations like the flight of pterosaur model serve any good purpose? Why or why not?

_____

_____

_____

_____

_____

2. What do you think scientists learn from projects like this? Why is it important to study animals that lived millions of years ago?

_____

_____

_____

_____

_____

DEVELOPING SPELLING SKILLS

Good spellers often use the dictionary to double-check certain words. If you know how to use a dictionary, looking up words can be done quickly and easily.

As you know, dictionaries are arranged in alphabetical order. At the top of each page are two *guide words*. These guide words help you find the page that lists the word you are looking up. The guide word on the left indicates the first word that is listed on that page. The guide word on the right indicates the last word listed on that page. You will find the word, or entry, that you are looking up in alphabetical order between the two guide words.

Examples: The word *essential* might be found between the guide words *essay* and *estate*.

The word *magnificent* might be found between the guide words *magnet* and *magnify*.

Some dictionaries also tell you how to pronounce the word, its part of speech, its definition, its history, synonyms, and other forms of the word.

Practice using the dictionary by looking up the words in the Study List.

SKILL DRILL 1

Write the following Study List words on the lines provided. Then circle the letter or letters that make each word difficult to spell.

1. congratulations _____
2. indefinitely _____
3. performance _____
4. surrounded _____
5. absence _____
6. analyze _____
7. equivalent _____

8. emergency _____
9. magnificent _____
10. situation _____
11. undoubtedly _____
12. accurate _____
13. coincidence _____
14. essential _____

15. guidance _____

SKILL DRILL 2

The following are short definitions of words from the Study List. Fill the blanks with words from the Study List that match the definitions. If you need help, check the Mini-Dictionary in the back of this book.

1. An act or deed that is performed _____
2. Splendid or very grand _____
3. Without any doubt _____
4. The state of being absent _____
5. Exactly right _____
6. Necessary; very important _____
7. Equal in value _____
8. A sudden need for immediate action _____
9. Expression of happiness for someone's good fortune _____
10. Enclosed on all sides _____
11. Not definitely _____
12. Position; location _____
13. Two things happening at the same time by accident _____
14. The act of guiding _____
15. To separate into parts and examine closely _____

SKILL DRILL 3

Fill the blanks in each of the following words to form words from the Study List. Then write the word you have formed on the line provided.

1. ab _ _ n _ _ _____
2. emer _ _ ncy _____
3. coin _ _ d _ _ ce _____
4. a _ _ urate _____
5. congra _ _ _ _ tions _____
6. anal _ _ e _____
7. equi _ _ _ _ nt _____

8. essen _ _ _ l _____
9. g _ _ d _ _ ce _____
10. indef _ _ _ _ ely _____
11. su _ _ ounded _____
12. magni _ _ c _ _ t _____
13. si _ _ a _ _ on _____
14. perform _ _ _ _ _____

15. undou _ _ edly _____

SKILL DRILL 4

Imagine that the words below are guide words in a dictionary. Write the words from the Study List that belong between each pair of guide words.

shepherd	1. _____	visible
	2. _____	
	3. _____	
analysis	4. _____	column
	5. _____	
distinguished	6. _____	eventually
	7. _____	
	8. _____	
confidence	9. _____	conscience
abbreviate	10. _____	accuse
	11. _____	
familiar	12. _____	January
	13. _____	
literature	14. _____	procedure
	15. _____	

WORD GAME 18

This is a crossword puzzle without clues! Study the length and spelling of each Study List word. Then figure out which words from the Study List fit in the spaces. Once you have found the first word, the rest will be easy to find. Some of the letters have been given to you.

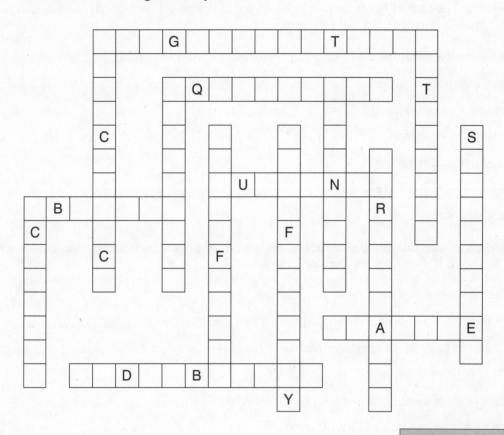

Study List

absence
accurate
analyze
coincidence
congratulations
emergency
equivalent
essential
guidance
indefinitely
magnificent
performance
situation
surrounded
undoubtedly

HOW WELL CAN YOU SPELL?

Try to take this practice test without looking back at Lesson 18. After you have finished, check your work against the Study List. Correct any mistakes you have made.

A. One word in each of the following pairs of words is spelled incorrectly. Circle that word and spell it correctly on the line provided.

1. undoutedly, surrounded   _____

2. performance, situayshun   _____

3. indefinitely, magnifisent   _____

4. guidence, essential   _____

5. equivelent, emergency   _____

6. coincidence, congragulations   _____

7. analize, accurate   _____

B. In each of the following sentences, one word is spelled incorrectly. Find that word. Then spell it correctly on the line provided.

8. No one could explain John's absince from class.   _____

9. A huge crowd surounded the singing performers.   _____

10. Deborah thought the performince was beautiful.   _____

11. This play will continue to run indefenitely.   _____

12. Proper daily exercise is essincial to good health.   _____

13. In an emergincy, we will exit through this door.   _____

14. Meeting Diana in the hallway was a nice coincidance.   _____

15. Please be sure that all of your answers are accurite. _____

CHALLENGE WORDS

Looking up words in the dictionary helps you remember how to spell them. Practice using the dictionary by looking up the Challenge Words below.

loneliness	absolutely	accidentally
sacrifice	practice	catalog
unmanageable	tendency	remembrance

Listening to Eudora

For 50 years, Eudora Welty has been writing short stories and novels. Her work has earned many honors. The Pulitzer Prize, the American Book Award, and the Gold Medal for the Novel are only a few of the awards she has received. Her work is so popular that she is known as the first lady of American fiction.

After five decades as a storyteller, Eudora has come to certain conclusions about writing. Many of her trade secrets can be found in her autobiography, *One Writer's Beginnings*. In this book, she points out how crucial *listening* is to writing. "Your ears should be like magnets," she says. "Long before I wrote stories, I listened for stories." Developing an ear for listening is very important. What a writer observes in life is the basis for fictional characters and situations. Eudora's characters are like real people we know or would like to know. "What I do in writing of any character is to try to enter into the mind, heart, and skin of a human being who is not myself," she explains. But the reader must contribute something as well. "The connection between the writer and the reader is very mysterious," says Eudora. "Both bring imagination to the work."

For Eudora, becoming a writer was no accident. It was a process that took many years and experiences. "It was my mother who supported me in my wish to become a writer," she says. And her father provided her first typewriter. Both parents encouraged her to attend college. There she became a reporter for the school paper. After graduation, she worked as a writer and photographer for local newspapers. These experiences paved the way for her career as an author.

Eudora's first fictional stories were not very popular. Nevertheless, she continued to write. Eventually her work began attracting attention. The rest is literary history. Stories like "Why I Live at the P.O." and books like *The Ponder Heart* have been delighting readers for years.

Recently, Mississippi celebrated Eudora's diamond jubilee. The occasion was her 75th birthday. It was declared Eudora Welty Day in her honor. Eudora said she was grateful for all the attention, but a little embarrassed. "I can just hear my mother saying, 'Girl, you're getting a little too much attention!'"

REVIEWING YOUR READING

Circle the letter beside the word or phrase that best completes the sentence.

1. Eudora Welty has been writing

    a. newspaper articles for 50 years.
    b. stories and novels for 50 years.
    c. news stories for 75 years.
    d. fictional stories for 75 years.

2. The honors Eudora Welty has earned include the

    a. Pulitzer Prize and the Gold Medal for the Novel.
    b. American Book Award and the Grammy Award.
    c. Pulitzer Prize and the Nobel Prize.
    d. Academy Award.

3. Eudora's autobiography is called

    a. *The Ponder Heart.*
    b. *Why I Live at the P.O.*
    c. *One Writer's Beginnings.*
    d. *Beginning to Write.*

4. According to Eudora, one of the most important things a writer must do is

    a. spell correctly.
    b. listen.
    c. learn other people's trade secrets.
    d. read carefully.

5. Eudora points out how crucial listening is to writing. The word *crucial* means

    a. unimportant.
    b. unnecessary.
    c. very important.
    d. creative.

6. Eudora has been writing stories for five decades. The word *decade* means

    a. years.
    b. centuries.
    c. a period of ten years.
    d. a period of 20 years.

7. According to the selection, you can conclude that Eudora's parents

    a. wanted her to become a photographer.
    b. encouraged her to write.
    c. discouraged her from attending college.
    d. wanted her to become a poet.

8. You can conclude that Eudora's stories

    a. all end happily.
    b. describe only family members.
    c. are based on real life.
    d. are all true.

FIGURING THE FACTS

Decide whether the following statements are true or false. Write *T* on the line if the statement is true. If the statement is false, change the statement to make it true. Cross out the incorrect word or phrase in the sentence. Then, if necessary, write the correct word or phrase on the line.

1. Recently, Eudora celebrated her diamond jubilee.   _____

2. A diamond jubilee is a celebration of one's 50th birthday.   _____

3. Eudora's home state is South Carolina.   _____

4. Eudora's first typewriter was given to her by her mother.   _____

5. At one time, Eudora worked as a photographer.   _____

6. Eudora believes that what a writer observes in life is the basis for fiction.   _____

7. Before Eudora ever wrote stories, she listened for them.   _____

8. One of Eudora's stories is "Why I Live at the P.O."   _____

9. In college, Eudora worked on the school yearbook.   _____

10. When writing, Eudora tries to get into the mind and heart of her characters.   _____

WHAT'S YOUR OPINION?

1. Why do you think learning to listen is so important to a writer?

_____

_____

_____

_____

2. Eudora believes that the reader and the writer both bring imagination to a story. Explain what she means by this.

_____

_____

_____

_____

DEVELOPING SPELLING SKILLS

Study List

admiration
appropriate
association
autobiography
continuous
embarrassed
imaginary
immediately
independent
interpretation
literary
occasion
permanent
possession
preferred

The following words appear in the reading selection.

autobiography   embarrassed   literary   occasion

Because these words are trickier to spell than other words, we call them "spelling demons." Experts have found that these are words people most often misspell. However, these demons are not really difficult to spell if we remember what makes each word tricky.

Examples: In the word *autobiography*, the leters *io* and *ph* are often misspelled.

In *embarrassed*, the double *r* and the double *s* are important to note.

In *literary*, the *a* is often mispronounced.

In *occasion*, it is important to remember that there is a double *c* and a single *s*.

Of course, you may think there are other tricky letters in some of these words. The most important thing for you to do is make a note of what makes the word difficult for you to spell.

Each word in the Study List is considered a spelling demon. Keep in mind that these are words that you will use often in your writing. Study them extra carefully. Be sure to note the letters in each word that make that word difficult for you to spell.

SKILL DRILL 1

Write the following Study List words on the lines provided. Then circle the letter or letters that make each word difficult to spell.

1. preferred _____

2. permanent _____

3. admiration _____

4. autobiography _____

5. literary _____

6. independent _____

7. imaginary _____

8. possession _____

9. occasion _____

10. association _____

11. continuous _____

12. interpretation _____

13. immediately _____

14. embarrassed _____

15. appropriate _____

SKILL DRILL 2

The following are short definitions of words from the Study List. Fill the blanks with words from the Study List that match the definitions. If you need help, check the Mini-Dictionary in the back of this book.

1. Lasting; not changing _____

2. A person's life story written by that person _____

3. A feeling of delight at something well done _____

4. Suitable or proper _____

5. A group of people joined together for some purpose _____

6. Not real; existing only in the imagination _____

7. Right now; as soon as possible _____

8. Not controlled by anyone _____

9. An explanation; the act of interpreting _____

10. A special event or day _____

11. Something that one owns _____

12. Liked or desired more than something else _____

13. Having to do with literature _____

14. To be disturbed or self-conscious _____

15. Happening without stopping; constant _____

SKILL DRILL 3

Fill the blanks in each of the following words to form words from the Study List. Then write the words you have formed on the lines provided.

1. im _ ed _ _ tely _____

2. emba _ _ a _ _ ed _____

3. auto _ _ _ graphy _____

4. ap _ _ _ pr _ _ te _____

5. prefe _ _ ed _____

6. perm _ n _ nt _____

7. lit _ r _ _ y _____

8. ima _ _ n _ ry _____

9. contin _ _ _ s _____

10. assoc _ _ tion _____

11. admir _ _ _ _ n _____

12. pos _ _ _ _ ion _____

13. o _ _ as _ _ n _____

14. inter _ _ _ _ ation _____

15. ind _ p _ _ d _ nt _____

SKILL DRILL 4

Answer the following questions by using words from the Study List.

Which words end with the suffix *ion*?

1. _____   2. _____

3. _____   4. _____

5. _____

Which words end with the suffix *ent*?

6. _____   7. _____

Which words being with the prefix *im* or *em*?

8. _____   9. _____

10. _____

Which words begin with the prefix *auto, con,* or *pre*?

11. _____   12. _____

13. _____

Which word ends with the suffix *ate*?

14. _____

Which eight-letter word ends with the suffix *ary*?

15. _____

WORD GAME 19

Use the words in the Study List to complete this crossword puzzle.

ACROSS

1. Liked more than something else
3. Happening without stopping
6. An explanation; the act of interpreting
7. Right now
9. A special event
11. A person's life story
12. Suitable or proper
13. A group of people joined together for some purpose

DOWN

1. Something that one owns
2. Not controlled by anyone
4. Not real
5. Having to do with literature
8. To be self-conscious or disturbed
10. A feeling of delight at something well done

Study List

admiration
appropriate
association
autobiography
continuous
embarrassed
imaginary
immediately
independent
interpretation
literary
occasion
permanent
possession
preferred

HOW WELL CAN YOU SPELL?

Try to take this practice test without looking back at Lesson 19. After you have finished, check your work against the Study List. Correct any mistakes you have made.

A. One word in each of the following pairs of words is spelled incorrectly. Circle that word and spell it correctly on the line provided.

1. imaginary, continuouse   _____

2. asociation, admiration   _____

3. indipendent, immediately   _____

4. occasion, interpetation   _____

5. possesion, preferred   _____

6. literary, perminent   _____

7. apropriate, autobiography   _____

B. In each of the following sentences, one word is spelled incorrectly. Find that word. Then spell it correctly on the line provided.

8. Diana prefered to walk rather than wait for the bus.   _____

9. The ocasion was to celebrate the anniversary of the club.   _____

10. The litrary club is raising money to buy books.   _____

11. When the crowd left, Rob immediatly began to clean up.   _____

12. The equator is an imaginery line around the earth.   _____

13. Gerry was imbarassed by all the questions he was asked.   _____

14. The doctor's autobiografy is fascinating.   _____

15. Ms. Valdez expressed her admeration for such good work.   _____

CHALLENGE WORDS

The Challenge Words below are spelling demons. Remember to note what it is in each word that makes it difficult for you.

innocence   circumstances   practically
particularly   ingenious   persuade
column   privilege   miniature

Tree People

As a teenager at summer camp, Andy Lipkis saw trees outside of the city dying from air pollution. Andy wanted to do something about it. He tried to get help from the government, but the answer was always the same: "You're just a kid. Come back when you're older."

A few years later, when he was a college sophomore, Andy learned that the California Division of Forestry was about to destroy thousands of unsold baby trees. Planting the trees would be very expensive. So destroying them seemed to be the only option. This time, Andy turned to a newspaper for help. When the story appeared in the paper, government officials were embarrassed. They agreed to give Andy 8,000 trees that had not yet been destroyed. With the help of the National Guard and a few thousand summer campers, the saplings were planted. A new forest sprang up from that planting. So did a new organization. It's called TreePeople.

TreePeople now has more than 2,000 members. Senior citizens, teenagers, the disabled, and Scout troops all work to save the environment. They volunteer to pot seeds, write newsletters, make calls, and, of course, plant trees. Recently, they planted one million trees in Los Angeles.

Like all plants, trees breathe continuously. This respiration process helps clean the air of pollution. The more trees a city has, the cleaner the air will be. Trees also prevent erosion of the earth's topsoil. Furthermore, they produce food and are beautiful to look at. What more could you ask for?

The members of TreePeople believe that education is the key to protecting the environment. Through classes and nature hikes, they hope to "inspire people to plant and care for trees." The plan seems to be working. Similar groups are taking root in Japan, Australia, and many other countries. There is even talk of a worldwide campaign to plant one billion new trees. But as Andy Lipkis will tell you, "TreePeople is not just for planting, but for uniting people in a cause."

REVIEWING YOUR READING

Circle the letter beside the word or phrase that best completes the sentence.

1. Andy Lipkis first noticed dying trees when he was

   a. a college sophomore.
   b. a teenager at summer camp.
   c. a candidate for government office.
   d. working for the Forestry Department.

2. TreePeople's first project was

   a. planting thousands of tiny trees.
   b. destroying thousands of tiny trees.
   c. cleaning up campgrounds.
   d. fighting with the National Guard.

3. Andy prevented the destruction of 8,000 baby trees by

   a. taking them into his home.
   b. buying them.
   c. getting help from a newspaper.
   d. alerting the National Guard.

4. Today, TreePeople has

   a. over 2,000 members.
   b. over 8,000 members.
   c. branches in every city.
   d. billions of trees to plant.

5. Destroying the trees seemed to be the only option. The word *option* means

   a. choice.
   b. method.
   c. burning.
   d. planting.

6. Trees breathe continuously. This respiration process cleans the air. The word *respiration* means

   a. cleaning.
   b. again and again.
   c. breathing.
   d. a way of doing something.

7. You can conclude that saplings are

   a. flowers.
   b. signposts.
   c. vines.
   d. baby trees.

8. You can conclude that the members of TreePeople believe that a good way to save the environment is through

   a. education.
   b. newsletters.
   c. cutting down old trees.
   d. political campaigns.

FIGURING THE FACTS

Decide whether the following statements are true or false. Write *T* on the line if the statement is true. If the statement is false, change the statement to make it true. Cross out the incorrect word or phrase in the sentence. Then, if necessary, write the correct word or phrase on the line.

1. The trees Andy saw were dying from pollution. _____

2. People told him he was too old to do anything about the problem. _____

3. Andy helped save 8,000 trees from destruction. _____

4. The 8,000 trees were planted by campers and the National Guard. _____

5. Anyone can be a member of TreePeople. _____

6. Volunteers plant trees and write newsletters. _____

7. Recently, they planted five billion trees in Los Angeles. _____

8. Someday the grown trees will help clean the air of pollution. _____

9. Trees help cause erosion. _____

10. Groups that are similar to TreePeople are forming in other countries. _____

WHAT'S YOUR OPINION?

1. What do you think Andy Lipkis means when he says, "TreePeople is not just for planting trees, but for uniting people in a cause"?

_____

_____

_____

_____

2. Why is it important to protect our environment?

_____

_____

_____

_____

DEVELOPING SPELLING SKILLS

Study List

calendar
campaign
erosion
government
interesting
maintenance
mischief
omitted
pollution
procedure
pronunciation
questionnaire
sophomore
straighten
volunteer

The following words are spelling demons that appear in the reading selection.

> *campaign   erosion   pollution*
> *sophomore   volunteer*

As you learn the words in this chapter, remember to make a mental note of what it is in each word that makes it difficult for you to spell.

Examples: In the word *campaign,* the letter *g* is easy to forget because it isn't pronounced.

In *erosion,* the *s* makes an unexpected sound, and the *i* isn't pronounced.

In *pollution,* it is important to remember the double *l.*

In *sophomore,* the second *o* often isn't pronounced.

In *volunteer,* remember the double *e.*

The words in the Study List are spelling demons. Remember to note what it is in each word that makes it difficult or confusing.

SKILL DRILL 1

Write the following Study List words on the lines provided. Then circle the letter or letters that make each word difficult to spell.

1. pollution _____
2. mischief _____
3. interesting _____
4. erosion _____
5. calendar _____
6. volunteer _____
7. straighten _____

8. omitted _____
9. maintenance _____
10. government _____
11. campaign _____
12. pronunciation _____
13. sophomore _____
14. questionnaire _____

15. procedure _____

SKILL DRILL 2

The following are short definitions of words from the Study List. Fill the blanks with words from the Study List that match the definitions. If you need help, check the Mini-Dictionary in the back of this book.

1. To have left something out _____
2. A second-year college student _____
3. The care or upkeep of something _____
4. The rule or authority over a country, state, etc. _____
5. A list of questions _____
6. A series of organized activities for a cause _____
7. A method of doing things _____
8. To make straight _____
9. A person who works without pay _____
10. A chart of dates and days of the year _____
11. The wearing away of the earth's topsoil _____
12. Poisons in the air and water _____
13. Stirring up interest _____
14. Conduct that usually causes trouble _____
15. A certain way of saying a word _____

SKILL DRILL 3

Fill the blanks in each of the following words to form words from the Study List. Then write the words you have formed on the lines provided.

1. so _ _ _ more _____

2. pol _ _ _ ion _____

3. m _ _ nten _ _ ce _____

4. go _ _ _ nment _____

5. calen _ _ _ _____

6. question _ _ _ re _____

7. proc _ _ _ re _____

8. vol _ _ _ eer _____

9. om _ _ _ ed _____

10. misch _ _ _ _____

11. inter _ _ _ ing _____

12. pro _ _ _ ciation _____

13. str _ _ _ _ _ en _____

14. ero _ _ _ _ _____

15. camp _ _ gn _____

SKILL DRILL 4

Answer the following questions by using words from the Study List.

Which words end with *ion*?

1. _____   2. _____   3. _____

Which words end with *re*?

4. _____   5. _____   6. _____

Which word ends with *eer*?

7. _____

Which word ends with *ar*?

8. _____

Which word contains the word *chief*?

9. _____

Which word contains the word *interest*?

10. _____

Which word contains the word *main*?

11. _____

Which word contains the word *camp*?

12. _____

Which word ends with the word *ten*?

13. _____

Which word contains the word *omit*?

14. _____

Which word ends with *ment*?

15. _____

WORD GAME 20

The words from the Study List are used in this puzzle. The numbers of the clues match the numbers in the puzzle. Read the clues below. Then write your answers in the puzzle blocks.

ACROSS

3. Loss of topsoil
4. Second-year student
6. Organized activities for a cause
8. A person who works for free
10. Left out
12. A list of questions
13. Trouble
14. Make straight
15. Upkeep

DOWN

1. Days and dates
2. Elected officials
5. Poisons in the air
7. Fascinating
9. A way of saying words
11. A method of doing things

Study List

calendar
campaign
erosion
government
interesting
maintenance
mischief
omitted
pollution
procedure
pronunciation
questionnaire
sophomore
straighten
volunteer

HOW WELL CAN YOU SPELL?

Try to take this practice test without looking back at Lesson 20. After you have finished, check your work against the Study List. Correct any mistakes you have made.

A. One word in each of the following pairs of words is spelled incorrectly. Circle that word and spell it correctly on the line provided.

1. pronounciation, calendar   _____

2. erosion, campane   _____

3. interesting, goverment   _____

4. manetenence, mischief   _____

5. omitted, polution   _____

6. proceedure, questionnaire   _____

7. sophmore, straighten   _____

B. In each of the following sentences, one word is spelled incorrectly. Find that word. Then spell it correctly on the line provided.

8. We need more students to voluntear for the band.   _____

9. Jack looked in the mirror and began to straiten his tie.   _____

10. Please fill out this questionaire and return it to me.   _____

11. Lois omited the part of her speech about war.   _____

12. Mr. Jackson knew the children would get into mischeif.   _____

13. Donald wrote a very inturesting composition about flying.   _____

14. Much of the topsoil was lost due to eroson.   _____

15. I will have to check my calender to see if I am free.   _____

CHALLENGE WORDS

Below are more spelling demons. Remember: Note what it is in each word that makes it difficult for you to spell.

fulfill	omission	acquaintance
instrument	laboratory	furniture
lightning	criticism	decision

MINI-DICTIONARY

A

absence *[AB suns]* the state of being absent

acceptable *[ak SEP tuh bul]* worth accepting

accompany *[uh KUM puh nee]* to go along with someone

accurate *[AK yur it]* exactly right

accuse *[uh KYOOZ]* to blame

achievement *[uh CHEEV munt]* an accomplishment or feat

acknowledge *[ak NOL ij]* to express thanks; to admit

admiration *[ad muh RAY shun]* a feeling of delight at something well done

admitted *[ad MIT id]* confessed that something was true

aisle *[EYEL]* the passage between rows of seats

analyze *[AN uh lyz]* to separate into parts and examine closely

ancient *[AYN shunt]* very old

anniversaries *[an uh VUR suh rees]* yearly celebrations

annually *[AN yoo ul lee]* yearly; every year

answered *[AN surd]* replied to a question

antonym *[AN tuh nim]* a word that means the opposite of another word

appropriate *[uh PROH pree it]* suitable or proper

article *[AR tih kul]* a certain thing or item

artificial *[ar tuh FISH ul]* not natural; false

artificially *[ar tuh FISH ul lee]* not naturally; not in a genuine way

artistically *[ar TIS tih kul lee]* in an artistic way

association *[uh soh see AY shun]* a group of people joined together for some purpose

athletically *[ath LET ih kul lee]* in an athletic manner

autobiography *[aw tuh by OG ruh fee]* a person's life story written by that person

autograph *[AW tuh graf]* a person's signature
Plural: **autographs** *[AW tuh grafs]*

B

basically *[BAY sik lee]* in a basic way

beige *[BAYZH]* a light tan color

belief *[bih LEEF]* a strong feeling about something
Plural: **beliefs** *[bih LEEFS]*

biscuits *[BIS kits]* cookies or crackers

buffalo *[BUF uh loh]* a bison; a large animal that roamed the plains of North America
Plural: **buffaloes** *[BUF uh lohs]*

C

cafeteria *[kaf ih TEER ee uh]* a self-service restaurant
Plural: **cafeterias** *[kaf ih TEER ee uhs]*

calendar *[KAL un dur]* a chart of dates and days of the year

campaign *[kam PAYN]* a series of organized activities for a cause

celebrity *[suh LEB rih tee]* famous person
plural: **celebrities** [suh LEB rih tees]

ceremony *[SER uh moh nee]* a formal or customary act like a wedding
Plural: **ceremonies** *[SER uh moh nees]*

characterize *[KAR ik tuh ryz]* to describe characteristics

charity *[CHAR ih tee]* help or relief for the poor
Plural: **charities** *[CHAR ih tees]*

chocolate *[CHAW kuh lit]* candy made from cocoa
Plural: **chocolates** *[CHAW kuh lits]*

circuit *[SUR kit]* a connection of electrical wires

circumference *[sur KUM fur uns]* the boundary line of a circle

coincidence *[koh IN sih duns]* two things happening at the same time by accident

commercial *[kuh MUR shul]* having to do with commerce; an advertisement

committed *[kuh MIT id]* devoted to a cause

committee *[kuh MIT ee]* a group of people who decide something

comparable *[KOM pur uh bul]* worthy of comparison

compatible *[kum PAT uh bul]* able to get along together

compelled *[kum PELD]* forced to do something

competition *[kom pih TISH un]* a type of athletic event

completed *[kum PLEET id]* finished

compromise *[KOM pruh myz]* the settlement of a dispute by both sides giving in

conceited *[kun SEE tid]* having too high an opinion of oneself

confirm *[kun FURM]* to prove something to be true or correct

congratulations *[kun grach uh LAY shuns]* expression of happiness for someone's good fortune

conjunction *[kun JUNGK shun]* a connecting word

conscience *[KON shuns]* the sense of right and wrong

considerable *[kun SID ur uh bul]* worth consideration; much or large

consulted *[kun SULT id]* asked for information or advice

continuous *[kun TIN yoo us]* happening without stopping; constant

contribution *[kun truh BYOO shun]* a gift or donation, usually money

controllable *[kun TROH luh bul]* able to be controlled

copy *[KOP ee]* a duplicate or reproduction
Plural: **copies** *[KOP ees]*

counterfeit *[KOUN tur fit]* not genuine; false

courteously *[KUR tee us lee]* graciously or politely

crystals *[KRIS tuls]* clear, transparent minerals that look like ice

cylinder *[SIL in dur]* a round object with two flat ends, such as a canister

---
D
---

deceive *[dih SEEV]* to make someone believe that something false is true

delayed *[dih LAYD]* postponed or put off until a later time

denied *[dih NYD]* stated that something was not true

dependable *[dih PEN duh bul]* able to be depended on

dictionaries *[DIK shuh ner ees]* books where definitions are found

disabilities *[dis uh BIL ih tees]* physical conditions that disable

discontinue *[dis kun TIN yoo]* to stop doing something

discussion *[dih SKUSH un]* a conversation or debate

disguise *[dis GYZ]* a mask or costume

dismayed *[dis MAYD]* greatly troubled

dispute *[dis SPYOOT]* an argument or discussion

dissolve *[dih ZOLV]* to melt or make into a liquid

division *[dih VIZH un]* the process of dividing one number into another

double *[DUB ul]* twice as much

E
---

economical *[ee kuh NOM ih kul]* thrifty; not wasteful

efficient *[ih FISH unt]* able to do something without waste

eligible *[EL ih juh bul]* fit to be chosen; qualified

embarrassed *[em BAR ust]* to be disturbed or self-conscious

emergency *[ih MUR jun see]* a sudden need for immediate action

encyclopedia *[en sy kluh PEE dee uh]* a book or set of books that gives information

endurance *[en DOOR uns]* the ability to last or keep going

engraved *[en GRAYVD]* carved into something

enormousness *[ih NOR mus nes]* hugeness

enthusiasm *[en THOO zee az um]* excitement or strong interest

envious *[EN vee us]* expressing envy; jealous

environment *[en VY run munt]* the world around you; your surroundings

equipped *[ih KWIPT]* provided with all that is needed

equivalent *[ih KWIV uh lunt]* equal in value

erosion *[ih ROH zhun]* the wearing away of the earth's topsoil

Eskimo *[ES kuh moh]* a member of a group of people who live near the North Pole
Plural: **Eskimos** *[ES kuh mohs]*

essential *[uh SEN shul]* necessary; very important

eventually *[ih VEN choo uh lee]* in the end; finally

experience *[ik SPEER ee uns]* knowledge that comes from doing something

exquisite *[EK skwih zit]* extremely beautiful

F

fascinating *[FAS uh nay ting]* extremely interesting

fictional *[FIK shun nul]* not real; made up

financial *[fih NAN shul]* having to do with money or finances

foreigner *[FOR uh nur]* a visitor from another country

forfeit *[FOR fit]* to give up as a penalty

fragile *[FRAJ ul]* easily broken; delicate

friendship *[FREND ship]* the state of being friends

fruitful *[FROOT ful]* plentiful; bearing fruit

G

generally *[JEN ur uh lee]* in most cases

government *[GUV urn munt]* the rule or authority over a country, state, etc.

graduation *[graj oo AY shun]* the completion of high school or college

groceries *[GROH suh rees]* food and supplies

guarantee *[gar un TEE]* a promise to pay or do something

guidance *[GYD uns]* the act of guiding

guilty *[GIL tee]* responsible for doing something wrong

guitar *[gih TAR]* a stringed instrument

gymnasium *[jim NAY zee um]* a place where people exercise

H

handicapped *[HAN dee kapt]* disadvantaged in some way

handkerchief *[HANG kur chif]* a piece of cloth used for wiping your face
Plural: **handkerchiefs** *[HANG kur chifs]*

historically *[hih STOR ih kul lee]* according to history

hurrying *[HUR ee ing]* rushing

hydrogen *[HY druh jun]* a gas or chemical

hygiene *[HY jeen]* rules of good health

hyphen *[HY fun]* a punctuation mark used to connect parts of a word

---

I

imaginary *[ih MAJ uh ner ee]* not real; existing only in the imagination

immediately *[ih MEE dee it lee]* right now; as soon as possible

importance *[im POR tuns]* significance; the state of being important

improvise *[IM pruh vyz]* to make something up without preparation

inconvenient *[in kun VEEN yunt]* not convenient

increasingly *[in KREE sing lee]* happening more and more

incredible *[in KRED uh bul]* difficult to believe; astonishing

indefinitely *[in DEF uh nit lee]* not definitely

indelible *[in DEL uh bul]* not erasable; permanent

independent *[in dih PEN dunt]* not controlled by anyone

influence *[IN floo uns]* power to affect another person

initial *[ih NISH ul]* the first or beginning

inspiring *[in SPYUR ing]* affecting one's emotions; influencing or causing

intelligence *[in TEL ih juns]* the ability to learn

interesting *[IN tur ih sting]* stirring up interest

interference *[in tur FEER uns]* the act of interfering or interrupting

interpretation *[in tur prih TAY shun]* an explanation; the act of interpreting

irresistible *[ir ih ZIS tuh bul]* not able to be resisted

irresponsible *[ir ih SPON suh bul]* not responsible

J

juiciest *[JOO see est]* the most juicy

K

kangaroo *[kang guh ROO]* an animal that hops and is found in Australia
Plural: **kangaroos** *[kang guh ROOS]*
kilometer *[KIL uh mee tur]* one thousand meters

L

legible *[LEJ uh bul]* able to be read
lengthwise *[LENGKTH wyz]* in the direction of the length
libraries *[LY brer ees]* places where books are kept
liquefying *[LIK wuh fy ing]* turning into a liquid
literary *[LIT uh rer ee]* having to do with literature
logically *[LOJ ih kul lee]* in a logical manner; reasonably

M

magnificent *[mag NIF ih sunt]* splendid or very grand
maintenance *[MAYN tuh nuns]* the care or upkeep of something
mathematically *[math uh MAT ih kul lee]* according to mathematics
melody *[MEL uh dee]* a tune or song
Plural: **melodies** *[MEL uh dees]*
memento *[muh MEN toh]* a souvenir
Plural: **mementos** *[muh MEN tohs]*
merchandise *[MUR chun dyz]* goods for sale
milligram *[MIL uh gram]* one thousandth of a gram
miscellaneous *[mis uh LAY nee us]* made up of many different parts
mischief *[MIS chif]* conduct that usually causes trouble
missile *[MIS ul]* a rocket that is projected into space

modernize

modernize *[MOD ur nyz]* to bring up to date or make modern
modified *[MOD uh fyd]* changed in some way
mosquito *[muh SKEE toh]* a flying insect that bites
Plural: **mosquitoes** *[muh SKEE tohs]*
multiplication *[mul tuh pluh KAY shun]* the process of multiplying one number by another
musically *[MYOO zih kul lee]* in a musical way
musician *[myoo ZISH un]* one who plays a musical instrument
mysterious *[mih STEER ee us]* full of mystery; hard to explain
mythology *[mih THOL uh jee]* the study of myths or legends

N

neighborhood *[NAY bur hood]* a place where people live
nervousness *[NUR vus nes]* the state of being restless or uneasy
noticeable *[NOH tih suh bul]* easily seen or noticed
notified *[NOH tuh fyd]* told or gave notice
nuisance *[NOO suns]* something that is annoying
numerous *[NOO mur us]* many

O

occasion *[uh KAY zhun]* a special event or day
occurred *[uh KURD]* happened or took place
official *[uh FISH ul]* a person who holds a public position
often *[AW fun]* frequent
omitted *[oh MIT id]* to have left something out
opportunity *[op ur TOO nih tee]* a favorable chance
Plural: **opportunities** *[op ur TOO nih tees]*
organize *[OR guh nyz]* to arrange in order

P

performance *[pur FOR muns]* an act or deed that is performed

permanent *[PUR muh nunt]* lasting; not changing

permitted *[pur MIT id]* allowed or gave permission

perpendicular *[pur pun DIK yuh lur]* a line at right angles to another line

personal *[PUR suh nul]* private; something individual

personality *[pur suh NAL ih tee]* the character of a person
Plural: **personalities** *[pur suh NAL ih tees]*

physically *[FIZ ih kul lee]* in a physical or bodily manner

politically *[puh LIT ih kul lee]* in a political manner

politician *[pol ih TISH un]* a person experienced in politics

pollution *[puh LOO shun]* poisons in the air and water

portfolio *[pohrtr FOH lee oh]* a case for carrying important papers
Plural: **portfolios** *[pohrt FOH lee ohs]*

portrayed *[pohr TRAYD]* acted or impersonated

possession *[puh ZESH un]* something that one owns

precious *[PRESH us]* valuable; much loved

preferred *[prih FURD]* liked or desired more than something else

previewing *[PREE vyoo ing]* looking at something beforehand

previously *[PREE vee us lee]* at an earlier time; formerly

procedure *[pruh SEE jur]* a method of doing things

procession *[pruh SESH un]* a parade; a group of people moving forward

professional *[pruh FESH uh nul]* a person who is in a certain field of work

pronunciation *[pruh nun see AY shun]* a certain way of saying a word

pursuit *[pur SOOT]* the act of chasing someone

Q

qualified *[KWOL uh fyd]* having the right qualifications

questionnaire *[kwes chuh NAIR]* a list of questions

quilted *[KWILT id]* sewn together with padding

R

received *[rih SEEVD]* to have taken something into your possession

receptacle *[rih SEP tuh kul]* a container for storing something

recommend *[rek uh MEND]* to give a suggestion

recommendation *[rek uh men DAY shun]* something that is recommended

recreation *[rek ree AY shun]* play or amusement

referred *[rih FURD]* directed attention to something

reflection *[rih FLEK shun]* an image in a mirror; serious thought

rehearsal *[rih HUR sul]* practice for a play

reigning *[RAYN ing]* ruling over people

reliable *[rih LY uh bul]* able to be relied on

remarkable *[rih MAR kuh bul]* worthy of comment

replied *[rih PLYD]* gave an answer

required *[rih KWYURD]* needed or demanded

rescue *[RES kyoo]* to save someone from danger

resemblance *[rih ZEM bluns]* likeness; similar in appearance

residue *[REZ ih doo]* what remains after a part is taken

respiration *[res puh RAY shun]* the act of breathing

responsibility *[rih spon suh BIL ih tee]* duty or obligation

revealed *[rih VEELD]* made a secret known

rhyme *[RYM]* the same sound at the ends of words or lines of poetry

rhythm *[RITH um]* regular repetition of a beat

ridiculous *[rih DIK yuh lus]* silly or laughable

S

sandwich *[SAND wich]* two pieces of bread with a filling
Plural: **sandwiches** *[SAND wich is]*

scenery *[SEE nuh ree]* an outdoor view

scissors *[SIZ urz]* a tool used for cutting

seasonal *[SEE zuh nul]* having to do with the seasons

sensible *[SEN suh bul]* having good judgment or sense

seriousness *[SEER ee us nes]* the quality of being serious

session *[SESH un]* the term or period of a meeting

several *[SEV ur ul]* a few

simple *[SIM pul]* easy to do or understand

simplifies *[SIM pluh fys]* makes something simpler

situation *[sich oo AY shun]* position; location

smudge *[SMUJ]* a smeared stain

solidify *[suh LID uh fy]* to harden or become solid

sophomore *[SOF uh mohr]* a second-year college student

spaghetti *[spuh GET ee]* a long, thin noodle
    Plural: **spaghetti** *[spuh GET ee]*

special *[SPESH ul]* distinctive; better than usual

species *[SPEE sheez]* a certain variety of something
    Plural: **species** *[SPEE sheez]*

spectacle *[SPEK tuh kul]* a very grand display

sterilize *[STER uh lyz]* to make free of germs

stitch *[STICH]* a loop of thread through cloth
    Plural: **stitches** *[STICH is]*

stomach *[STUM uk]* part of the body used for digestion

straighten *[STRAYT un]* to make straight

studiousness *[STOO dee us nes]* devotion to study

submitted *[sub MIT id]* offered for consideration

substitution *[sub stih TOO shun]* the act of putting one thing in place of another

subterranean *[sub tuh RAY nee un]* underground

subtraction *[sub TRAK shun]* the process of subtracting one number from another

sufficient *[suh FISH unt]* as much as is needed; enough

suggestion *[sug JES chun]* something that is suggested

surrounded *[suh ROUND id]* enclosed on all sides

survival *[sur VY vul]* the act of surviving or lasting

suspiciously *[suh SPISH us lee]* in a suspicious way

symbolic *[sim BOL ik]* used as a symbol of something

sympathetic *[sim puh THET ik]* having or showing kind feelings toward others

synonym *[SIN uh nim]* a word that means the same as another word

synthetic *[sin THET ik]* artificial

T

territory *[TER ih tohr ee]* an area of land
    Plural: **territories** *[TER ih tohr ees]*

thief *[THEEF]* someone who steals
    Plural: **thieves** *[THEEVS]*

tissue *[TISH oo]* a mass of cells

tomato *[tuh MAY toh]* a juicy, red fruit, often used as a vegetable
    Plural: **tomatoes** *[tuh MAY tohs]*

tongue *[TUNG]* part of the body used for speaking

tornado *[tor NAY doh]* a large storm that has funnel-like clouds
    Plural: **tornadoes** *[tor NAY dohs]*

transferred *[TRANS furd]* moved something from one place to another

transition *[tran ZISH un]* the act of changing from one thing to another

tremendously *[trih MEN dus lee]* enormously

typhoon *[ty FOON]* a violent storm; a cyclone

typically *[TIP ih kul lee]* in a typical manner

U

unconsciously *[un KON shus lee]* not consciously

undoubtedly *[un DOU tid lee]* without any doubt

unexpected *[un ik SPEK tid]* not expected; surprising

unnecessary *[un NES ih ser ee]* not really needed

unsatisfactory *[un sat is FAK tuh ree]* not good enough to satisfy

usually *[YOO zhoo ul lee]* in a usual way

V

valuable *[VAL yoo uh bul]* having great worth

vanished *[VAN ishd]* disappeared

various *[VAR ee us]* many kinds; different

vigorously *[VIG ur us lee]* forcefully or energetically

vocalist *[VOH kuh list]* singer

volcano *[vol KAY noh]* a mountain that has erupted
    Plural: **volcanoes** *[vol KAY nohs]*

volunteer *[vol un TEER]* a person who works
without pay

---W---

wrench *[RENCH]* a tool used to loosen or tighten
bolts
Plural: **wrenches** *[RENCH is]*

---Y---

yourself *[yoor SELF]* you; your being
Plural: **yourselves** *[yoor SELVZ]*